W9-ASP-557

ECHOES OF BATS AND MEN

DONALD R. GRIFFIN was born in 1915 in Southampton, New York. He was educated at Phillips Academy, Andover, Massachusetts, and at Harvard University (B.S., 1938; M.A., 1940; Ph.D., 1942), where he was variously Junior Fellow and Research Associate until 1946. Griffin taught physiology and zoology at Cornell University until 1953, when he returned to Harvard to teach elementary zoology and served as Chairman of the Department of Biology from 1962 to 1965. Since then he has been Professor at the Rockefeller University in New York and Director of the Institute for Research in Animal Behavior, jointly sponsored by the New York Zoological Society and the Rockefeller University.

His enthusiasm for science began as a boy when he lived on Cape Cod. "I always found small mammals enough like ourselves," Griffin says, "to feel that I could understand what their lives would be like, and yet different enough to make it a sort of adventure and exploration to see what they were doing. College courses plus reading and conversations with an unusually wise and stimulating group of friends and advisers led my interests to include the physiological mechanisms that operate in the bodies of animals and men."

Since it soon became clear to him that many of the problems of biology might be solved by direct application of the methods and instruments of physics, he began, first, to band bats, then to study and record the ultrasonic cries with which they navigate. "By a most fortunate accident," he says, "I was a student at Harvard College, where, in 1938, one of the few physicists then actively studying sounds above the range of human hearing was willing to let my bats register their ultrasonic sounds on his apparatus. This was G. W. Pierce, and a casual visit to his laboratory with a cage full of bats began the line of research that forms the subject of this book.

"In the same years," he continues, "I was also studying migratory birds, first by homing experiments in which they were carried some distance from their nests and released. Many of the sea birds studied in this way (herring gulls, terns, petrels, and gannets) found their way home. But homing experiments only tell the time required and the percentage returning at all. So I decided to learn to fly myself and trace the actual routes flown. I managed to do this with a number of gulls and gannets, circling in a Piper Cub for as long as ten hours at a stretch while the bird did its cross-country flying." During World War II Griffin applied the biophysical approach to projects for the development of equipment for the Armed Forces–headphones and microphones for communications, cold-weather clothing and electric suits for fliers, and studies of human vision in the infrared which were basic to the design of the infrared snooperscope viewer.

Griffin's work, which has so advantageously combined physics and biology, has caused him to feel that his own introduction to biology and physics could have been greatly improved upon, that his early education encouraged the misconception that "physics was the more difficult and erudite of the two, and that biology was the catching, naming, and cataloguing of innumerable varieties of animals and plants." His later experience and research have forcibly demonstrated that working simultaneously with both sciences yields original and valuable results. In fact, these studies have, Griffin says, uncovered "new problems faster than I or anyone else has been able to solve the old ones. I am now beginning to suspect that living mechanisms operate in ways that are so intricate and marvelous that if we finally understand them, we will, in the process, have extended the horizons of physics."

ECHOES OF BATS AND MEN

Donald R. Griffin

Published by
Anchor Books
Doubleday & Company, Inc.
Garden City, New York

Back cover photograph by Ollie Atkins. Reprinted by special permission of *The Saturday Evening Post,* Curtis Publishing Company, 1955. Cover design by George Giusti. Typography by Edward Gorey.

Library of Congress Catalog Card Number 59–12051

THE SCIENCE STUDY SERIES

The Science Study Series offers to students and to the general public the writing of distinguished authors on the most stirring and fundamental topics of physics, from the smallest known particles to the whole universe. Some of the books tell of the role of physics in the world of man, his technology and civilization. Others are biographical in nature, telling the fascinating stories of the great discoverers and their discoveries. All the authors have been selected both for expertness in the fields they discuss and for ability to communicate their special knowledge and their own views in an interesting way. The primary purpose of these books is to provide a survey of physics within the grasp of the young student or the layman. Many of the books, it is hoped, will encourage the reader to make his own investigations of natural phenomena.

These books are published as part of a fresh approach to the teaching and study of physics. At the Massachusetts Institute of Technology during 1956 a group of physicists, high school teachers, journalists, apparatus designers, film producers, and other specialists organized the Physical Science Study Committee, now operating as a part of Educational Services Incorporated, Watertown, Massachusetts. They pooled their knowledge and experience toward the design and creation of aids to the learning of physics. Initially their effort was supported by the National Science Foundation, which has continued to aid the program. The Ford Foundation, the Fund for the Advancement of Education, and the Alfred P. Sloan Foundation have also given support. The Committee is creating a textbook, an extensive film series, a laboratory guide, especially designed apparatus, and a teacher's source book for a new integrated secondary school physics program which is undergoing continuous evaluation with secondary school teachers.

The Series is guided by the Board of Editors, consisting of Paul F. Brandwein, the Conservation Foundation and Harcourt, Brace and Company; John H. Durston, Educational Services Incorporated; Francis L. Friedman, Massachusetts Institute of Technology; Samuel A. Goudsmit, Brookhaven National Laboratory; Bruce F. Kingsbury, Educational Services Incorporated; Philippe LeCorbeiller, Harvard University; Gerard Piel, *Scientific American;* and Herbert S. Zim, Simon and Schuster, Inc.

PREFACE

Physical principles operate, as far as we know, throughout a universe which has both astronomical dimensions and a fine grain, some of it close at hand. New horizons can be large and distant or they may lie in the very small and commonplace. The unique properties of water molecules present just as interesting, even awesome, phenomena as does the history of stellar galaxies. And in between, accessible for convenient study, is a delightful variety of ingenious mechanisms making up the living bodies of plants and animals. Man has been said to "stand between the atoms and the stars," and between molecules and men are to be found many fascinating applications of physics, broadly conceived. Outstanding among these are the ways in which living organisms utilize wave motion of various kinds. Of particular interest is the interplay between sound waves and the animals and men who use them.

Sound waves can tell us a great deal about the world around us, and they are often used for this purpose by both animals and men. Sound exhibits all the properties of wave motion, and these properties can be observed whenever sound travels back and forth from place to place carrying information about the things it touches. This is obviously true when people talk to one another or when birds call from the treetops. But sound waves are also useful as messengers when only one person or animal is present to broadcast them and listen for their echoes a short time later. It is especially stimulating to examine the many effective ways in which animals make use of echoes, and to compare these with artificial devices which operate on the same basic principles. This comparison illustrates the important fact that some of the most difficult scientific questions have been solved by co-operation between different branches of science or technology. A century-old mystery of zoology was largely dispelled by one afternoon in the appropriate physics laboratory. And physicists faced with discouraging practical problems are inspired to believe that their tasks are not quite hopeless when they consider the accomplishments of even the smallest living brains.

Finally, there is the hope, still far from realization, that full and proper use of the physics and biology of echoes may serve to lessen the handicap of blindness. For what blind men attempt crudely, in finding their way about in a world of darkness, specialized animals accomplish with truly marvelous skill and efficiency Electronic instruments also accomplish the seemingly impossible by detecting invisible targets at great distances. There is an important unity in the role which echoes play in the biology, psychology, and physics of orientation.

This account of fruitful co-operation among many different kinds of scientists has drawn upon much of their published work. Some of this material is discussed at greater length in *Listening in the Dark,* and I am grateful to the editors of the Yale University Press for permission to use part of its subject matter. Readers interested in more detailed information will also find helpful references in the short bibliography on page 147. I have received many helpful suggestions from the staff of the Physical Science Study Committee. A large number of companions and colleagues have participated in my own observations and experiments, and their aid and

ncouragement were essential for the experiments de-
cribed in Chapters 1 and 4. Finally, I am happy to
cknowledge the patience and understanding of my wife
nd children who gave up many activities they would
ave much preferred to listening to my typewriter.

CONTENTS

ECHOES OF BATS AND MEN

CHAPTER 1

Voices of Experience

Doing something in the dark is almost always difficult; the darker it is the more troublesome an otherwise simple task becomes. Worst of all is to be blind. It is also a formidable task to build machines to trace the movements of distant objects which we cannot see—airplanes flying above the clouds or submarines hundreds of feet below the surface of the ocean. Finding your way on a dark night is obviously related to the problems of readjusting to a life of blindness, and instruments for searching out invisible targets must solve similar problems. All these solutions are based on the sending out of some form of energy and the sensing of a part of this energy as it echoes back from the object at a distance.

When we wish to learn about a difficult subject, such as the use of waves for searching out the invisible, we naturally look first for an expert who can explain its complexities for our benefit. There are experts who have extensive practical experience in the use of echoes. Some of them make their living using echoes to locate small moving objects which they cannot see. One group are the physicists and engineers who design and operate radar and sonar systems, complicated mechanisms which send out radio waves or sound waves to locate objects that return echoes of these probing signals. These systems will be discussed later, but the present chapter will be devoted to another group of experts who can draw upon a longer history of realistic, operational experience —experts who use echoes not only to find their way but also to obtain their daily bread and butter. If their systems should fail, they would starve to death, and this pressure of necessity has led to great refinement and reliability of their methods.

These experts are animals which live where sound replaces light as the best means of finding their way— caves where bats fly by the thousands, or dark waters where light is nearly nonexistent or is so diffused that clear images over any distance are impossible. The best known of these animal experts are the whales and porpoises, which often swim in dark or turbid waters, catching fish they cannot see, and the bats, which fly in near or total darkness, getting all their food by aerial interception of invisible flying insects. To have survived at all required of these animals and their ancestors enormous skill at echolocation, the location of objects by their echoes. By studying the sounds they use and how they modify them for particular problems of echolocation, we may learn much that can help blind people. Even aside from this reason, we will find these animals' use of echoes to be a fascinating subject in its own right.

Echo Experts in the Ocean

Only in the clearest water does light travel far enough in straight lines so that objects can be seen at more than a few feet. Daylight cannot penetrate nearly to the bottom of the ocean, though this does not mean, as people used to believe, that the ocean depths are totally dark. Oceanographers have recently discovered that luminescent animals are so numerous that a sufficiently sensitive light meter can register the flashes of light they give off when the meter is lowered far below the deepest penetration of sunlight. On the other hand, many rivers and lakes contain enough sediment so that clear vision is impossible for more than a few inches even in daylight. Yet hosts of fish and other aquatic animals live active lives in these waters where vision is nearly impossible, and it is not surprising that some have turned to sound as a medium of communication and a means of orientation, for sound travels farther in water than does light.

We usually think of the oceans and deep fresh-water streams and lakes (those without outboard motors) as silent, and few people even realize that fish or whales can hear. The chief reason is that our own hearing mechanism is designed primarily for use in air and so does not function well in water. Our ears can detect an airborne sound so faint that it approaches the noise level rising from random motion of molecules. The eardrums and the chain of little bones and elastic tissue that convey sound waves to our inner ear mechanisms are beautifully adapted to accept sound waves arriving through the air, but poorly suited to receive them from the water. When we do hear sounds under water, much of the acoustic energy flows directly from the water through our bodies, which are largely composed of water, to the sensitive portions of the inner ear, where minute vibrations stimulate the auditory nerve.

Sound waves do not move easily from air to water, or vice versa. The boundary between a gas and a liquid acts as an almost impenetrable barrier, and more than 99 per cent of the sound energy is reflected back into whichever medium conveyed it to the surface. That is, airborne sound waves are reflected back almost totally from the water, and underwater sound is equally well reflected back downward from the surface. Even if we dive beneath the water, we do not hear as well as fish can. This helps to explain why the noises made by certain fish and whales are so seldom noticed, though they have been known for centuries to fishermen and whalers. Even biologists have been slow to realize that fish can hear underwater sounds. Nevertheless, all fish have inner ears basically similar to our own, and while the sound waves reach these auditory sense organs by different routes (through the body itself rather than through air-filled canals), they stimulate the auditory nerve in very nearly the same way.

At frequencies up to about 1000 cycles per second (c.p.s.) the minimum amount of sound energy audible to a catfish is below the minimum energy detectable by the human ear. This includes the range of many musical instruments and the fundamental pitch of the human voice. At higher frequencies fish are less sensitive to sounds than we are, but their hearing is not inferior to that of land animals in any basic way.

An ability to hear underwater sounds is still far removed from the blind man's problem of learning how to use echoes for obtaining more information about his surroundings. With fish there is only suggestive evidence that certain species may utilize echoes. But marine mammals, the whales and porpoises, are not only more closely related to ourselves but also have brains that are as large or larger than human brains and equally complex, at least in their structure. Their inner ears and larynx are well developed, and the auditory portions are if anything more prominent in the whale brain than in our own. Nor are they silent creatures. Once proper equipment was available for converting underwater sound to audible, airborne sound, porpoises were found to be positively garrulous. An individual porpoise has a large "vocabulary" of squeals, whistles, grunts, and rasping, clicking sounds. While fishermen and whalers had heard some of these sounds from time to time, it was only during the last war that underwater listening became refined enough and common enough to reveal the immense variety of sounds used by the marine mammals. Many of these calls are alarm signals or convey simple messages from one porpoise to another, but some are clearly used for echolocation.

In recent experiments individual porpoises have been isolated in small ponds or experimental tanks, such as those at the larger marine aquaria of Florida and California. When obstacles are set up in such a tank, the porpoises are able to dodge them at high speed, even when the obstacles are put into place on the darkest nights. While doing this, porpoises make sounds of various sorts, usually faint clicking sounds that were overlooked at first because they were masked by incidental noises in the ponds. Most porpoises spend their lives in the open ocean, but there are a few smaller kinds which live in the larger and often very muddy rivers, such as the Amazon in South America and the Ganges in India. These animals must often thread their way among underwater obstructions, such as logs and fallen trees. Even the species that live in open waters continue their activities at night. All porpoises feed on fish, which they must catch by active pursuit, much of the time in poor light where it is impossible to see clearly more than a few centimeters. Therefore, it is not surprising that the most impressive feats of underwater echolocation have been exhibited in the capture of fish by hungry porpoises.

Captive porpoises are usually fed by tossing dead fish

into their tank–they soon learn to swim directly to the splash from wherever they may be. The eager approach of the hungry porpoise could be explained as a simple localization of the "loud" splash which they had learned meant food. But two careful experimenters, William Schevill and Barbara Lawrence (Mrs. Schevill), working at the Woods Hole Oceanographic Institution, Woods Hole, Massachusetts, in 1955, noticed that their captive porpoise found small, silent bits of food by echolocation. The porpoise spent much time searching the pond for food, and in doing so he emitted faint creaking noises which could be detected only with sensitive underwater listening equipment. They were not audible to a person listening from the bank of the pond or to a swimmer with his head under water. The creaking consisted of a series of clicks repeated at varying rates, sometimes so fast as to become a grating rasp or buzz. Suspecting that the animal might be listening for echoes from fish, Schevill and Lawrence sought to learn whether he could detect and recognize a small dead fish by echolocation and, if so, at what approximate distance. To eliminate vision, they frequently worked on dark nights, and in any case their experimental pond, only about 20 meters (about 65.6 feet) in diameter, was stirred into a muddy soup by the constant swimming of the porpoise. Even a brightly painted piece of metal became invisible in bright sunlight when immersed to a depth of about 60 centimeters (about 23.6 inches).

When a man sitting in a small boat tied to the shore quietly held a dead fish a few centimeters under water, the porpoise learned to swim toward it, "creaking" all the time, and seize the morsel. To make the test more critical as far as the distance of detection was concerned, a fish net was placed perpendicular to the bank, as shown in Fig. 1. The net extended out 2.4 meters from

Fig. 1. This shows the arrangement of boat and net in the porpoise echolocation experiments of W. E. Schevill and B. Lawrence.

the boat, and the porpoise had to decide at more than that distance which side of the net to choose in swimming up to the boat where food might be expected. He was fed irregularly, sometimes at one end of the boat, sometimes at the other, but in cruising past under water on a dark night he would almost never turn in closer to the bank than the end of the net unless a fish was being held beneath the surface. If the porpoise was not "creaking" as he swam past, he did not swim toward the boat even when a fish was offered.

For the most significant experiments Schevill and Lawrence sat at opposite ends of the anchored boat, each holding a fish at arm's length as the hungry porpoise swam past through the dark and murky water. Sometimes one and sometimes the other would gently and silently slip a 15-centimeter fish just below the surface, and if the hungry porpoise was "creaking" as he passed by, he would usually swim in to pick up his fish. In about three quarters of the tests he would choose the correct side of the net, even though he had been accustomed to pick up his food about equally often at either end of the anchored skiff.

This and other experiments show that porpoises can do more than simply detect isolated echoes of their creaking sounds from objects as small as 15-centimeter fish. More impressive still, they can discriminate one echo out of many others from all the submerged objects within range. Captive porpoises have learned to distinguish one favorite kind of fish from others of slightly different size by their echo patterns.

If a porpoise can echolocate a 15-centimeter fish, what prevents a blind man from hearing echoes from objects of similar size that lie on the floor or on a table? Actually there are several factors which work to the disadvantage of the porpoise. Sound travels about four and one half times faster in water than in air, so that the time differences between echoes from objects at different distances are that much smaller and presumably that much harder to detect. Furthermore, fish are very similar to water in the way they affect sound waves, and most of the energy of underwater sound that strikes a fish continues through its watery body just as though no fish were there. The same physical problem is present in the body and hearing apparatus of the porpoise; it too is nearly "transparent" to underwater sound, and it is intrinsically difficult for sound waves to interact with the various parts of its body. Indeed, it is likely that in the experiments of Schevill and Lawrence the echoes used by the porpoise came not so much from the 15-centimeter fish as from its small air-filled swim bladder, which reflected sound much as an air bubble would do. It would take us too far afield to present all the physical properties of underwater sound that are important for this extremely skillful echolocation by porpoises, but the interested reader may refer to Chapter 10 of *Listening in the Dark* (see Further Reading).

Two facts may help to explain the precision with which porpoises detect echoes from fish: one is the wide frequency range of their emitted sounds, and the other the range of their hearing. Tests have shown that they hear sounds as low in frequency as 150 c.p.s. and as high as 150,000 c.p.s. Yet these may not be the true limits of their hearing but only those set by the apparatus used to test it. In water where the velocity of sound is some four and one half times that in air, sound waves of 150,000 c.p.s. have a shorter wave length than the highest frequencies to which human ears have really useful sensitivity. Except by young children, it is doubtful whether frequencies above 15,000 c.p.s. are heard well enough to be useful for detecting objects by their echoes. The tenfold increase in the highest audible frequencies slightly more than offsets the increase in wave length of sound in water. Thus we should expect the porpoise to have only about a twofold advantage over a blind man owing to the shorter wave lengths that lie within his repertoire of echo-generating sounds. Factors other than wave length must therefore explain the expertness of porpoises at the art of echolocation, which blind men, as we shall see in Chapter 6, also try to cultivate. Perhaps they have simply learned individually to pay more attention to echoes, or perhaps in their long evolutionary history they have acquired ears and brains that are better adapted in some way we do not understand for sorting out echo components from the complex mixture of sounds bombarding their ears.

Echo Experts in the Air

Porpoises are large, spectacular, exotic, and it is relatively easy to accept the fact that they are capable of doing wonders in their watery world. At large outdoor aquaria they are trained to perform such circus tricks as leaping out of the water through burning hoops, catching rubber balls or dead fish tossed to them by their trainers, and even throwing something back to a particular person in the audience. No one who has ever watched these performances, or even motion pictures of them, can doubt the intelligence, agility, or skill of porpoises. But they do live in the water rather than in our medium, the air. Consequently they seem somewhat more remote from the blind man's problems than the other major group of animals which make extensive use of echoes in their daily lives. These are the bats–tiny mysterious creatures and, let's face it, to many people repulsive ones. Furry little mammals, resembling mice except for their wings, they prefer darkness, are quite at home in the blackest caves and generally encountered only as unwanted invaders of attic or summer cottage. At first glance nothing would seem to be more remote from any humanitarian contribution to the biophysics of orientation of blind human beings.

It is the startling strangeness of bats, plus the folklore that couples them with demons and the nether regions, which makes it so hard to think of them with anything other than repugnance. But they are experts in the use of echoes, and if we wish to find out what can be learned about objects from echoes, we must be prepared to accept important evidence regardless of our feelings about its source. It would be a real oversight to ignore the skills attained by bats in guiding their rapid flight by means of echoes.

Our knowledge of bat navigation really started in 1793 when the brilliant Italian scientist Lazzaro Spallanzani became interested in how various animals found their way about in darkness. Owls and other nocturnal creatures, he found, were relying on their large eyes, and they became helpless in complete darkness. But when he experimented with bats, he was puzzled to discover that they continued to fly almost perfectly when they could not possibly see a thing. Not content with experiments in which they flitted unconcernedly through the darkest chambers he could find, he finally resorted to blinding several bats. Even then they flew as well as ever. He released a number of blinded bats out of doors and looked for them four days later in the bell tower of the cathedral at Pavia, where he had caught them for his experiments in the first place. Wishing to know whether they had been able to continue their ordinary activities without their eyes, he climbed up to the bell tower early in the morning just after the bats' usual time for returning from a night of active flight and food gathering. Like all bats that are found in temperate climates, these fed exclusively on insects, flying insects which they had to pursue and catch on the wing. Spallanzani caught four of the bats he had blinded a few days earlier, and on dissecting them found that their stomachs were just as tightly crammed with the remains of insects as the other bats, which had not been blinded.

Spallanzani performed a number of other experiments, which, together with those of the Swiss biologist Charles Jurine, led him to conclude before his death in 1799 that, while bats could dispense with their eyes, any serious impairment of their hearing was disastrous. When their ears were plugged, they collided blindly and at random with whatever obstacles were set in their way. Only a really tight closure of the ear canals sufficed to produce total disorientation, but Spallanzani's experiments were completely convincing. One example of the ingenuity of his methods was the way he investigated the possibility that the bats' navigation might be disturbed by irritation or injury caused by the earplugs rather than by interference with hearing. He had some tiny brass tubes constructed and fitted them into the ear openings of the bats. This was no easy job in the 1790s since bats' ear canals are less than one millimeter in diameter. When the tubes were in place but open, the bats could still fly with almost normal skill. When the same tubes were tightly plugged, they caused no greater irritation, yet the bats were now wholly disoriented and bumped at random into every obstacle. No matter which of several methods he used to close the ear openings, if the closure was a tight one, the bat was helpless.

On the other hand, a wide variety of other experiments disclosed no effect of impairment of other sense organs–vision, touch, smell, or taste. But these findings seemed to make no sense, for the bats were completely silent as far as anyone could tell, both before and after they had been subjected to these various experimental treatments. How could the ears replace the eyes in guiding their flight? In 1800 there seemed to be no answer to this question, and Spallanzani's findings were rejected, ridiculed, and almost totally forgotten. Armchair critics surmised that some refined sense of touch, probably located on the wing membranes, accounted for bats' ability to detect objects at a distance and thus avoid them, but no one even tried to explain how Spallanzani's four blinded bats had filled their stomachs with flying insects.

What came to be called "Spallanzani's bat problem" was not solved for 140 years after his death when electronic apparatus had been developed at Harvard by the physicist G. W. Pierce to detect sounds lying outside the frequency range of human hearing. Just as soon as I brought some bats to Pierce's apparatus, it became obvious that they were emitting plenty of sound, but that it was almost entirely above the frequencies that we could hear. Further experiments, in collaboration with Robert Galambos, now Professor of Psychology at Yale University, demonstrated that covering the mouth of a bat and thus preventing its emission of these high-frequency sounds was just as effective as plugging its ears. Both treatments made bats quite unable to detect large objects or small, and they bumped against the walls of the room or anything else in their path. In short, their whole orientation during flight depended upon echoes of the high-frequency sounds that they emitted almost continuously while flying about. Because these sounds have shorter wave lengths, and consequently higher frequencies, than those to which our ears respond, the ability of bats to fly in total darkness had seemed a complete mystery. But once this simple fact became known, all seemed clear, at least in its broad outlines.

As a matter of fact, the sounds with which bats guide their flight are not totally inaudible. While more than 99.9 per cent of the sound energy emitted by bats that have been studied most thoroughly is at frequencies above the human range, there is also a faint audible component. It is so faint that one is likely to suspect the sounds come from the fluttering of the wings, and, in fact, they were overlooked by Spallanzani. Whenever a bat emits a burst of very high-frequency sound which can be detected by suitable electronic apparatus, one can also hear a faint tick accompanying each of them. Perhaps some readers may have an opportunity to watch and listen to bats on a warm evening. The bats found in temperate climates often roost in crevices in buildings and fly out every evening between sunset and complete darkness. If one stands close to where they fly (1 to 2 meters), and if it is really quiet and you can refrain from squealing, you can hear these ticking sounds. The younger you are, the more easily you can hear them, for even the audible component has a frequency of roughly 5000 to 10,000 cycles per second. There are also a few kinds of tropical, fruit-eating bats which make clearly audible ticks when they fly in dark caves. Where there is any light they use their eyes, which are much larger than those of the insectivorous bats. Two kinds of cave-dwelling birds also click loudly when flying in complete darkness but rely on vision at other times.

The faint ticking component of a bat's orientation sound is of very short duration, not unlike the ticking of a lady's wrist watch. But, unlike a watch, the bat's ticks will vary markedly in their tempo. If it is flying straight at some obstacles from a distance, there may be from five to twenty ticks per second. But if the bat is faced with complicated navigational problems, such as dodging you or a stick which you hold up in front of you, you may hear the ticking suddenly increase until it forms a faint buzz. The same thing happens just before a bat makes a landing, but the audible ticks are such a faint sound that it requires patience and completely quiet surroundings for them to be heard. The auditory basis of obstacle detection by bats was independently recognized in 1942 by a Dutch zoologist, Sven Dijkgraaf, who made a careful study of these faint, audible clicks and noted how closely they were correlated with the echolocation of obstacles. This is an example of the need for care, patience, and appropriate conditions if one is to notice and enjoy some of the more fascinating facets of the natural world.

Bats are not always agile and clever fliers; sometimes they are sleepy and clumsy—especially when they have been disturbed in the daytime. Most American and European species tend to let their body temperature fall to about that of the air in which they sleep. In winter many kinds of bats hibernate in caves or other places where they find temperatures only a few degrees above freezing. At such temperatures they are completely torpid, and one may easily think them dead. In between deep hibernation and full activity are many degrees of activity and alertness. The bats we are most likely to find and have an opportunity to observe are usually those that are least agile and least ready to display their full repertoire of flight maneuvers. If fully airworthy, they would be unlikely to let us watch them for long at close range. Furthermore, they often seem to become tired, and when chased about a room or attic they may soon become clumsy from fatigue alone. But if one takes the trouble to observe bats at their best, when fully awake and in top flying condition, as they are every night of normal summer insect hunting, then their agility and finesse at flying through complicated pathways are truly amazing. Flitting between the rungs of a chair is easy for an animal which naturally flies between the smaller branches of pine trees on the darkest nights.

After considering these two expert practitioners of echolocation and before moving ahead, let us put ourselves back into the frame of mind in which Spallanzani must have viewed these phenomena. From curiosity about the vision of nocturnal animals he had been led to perform a long series of careful and critical experiments with bats. While he could hear no sound as they flew about, he had convinced himself, despite his strong initial skepticism, that the ears and not the eyes were the sense organs that informed bats about such small objects as threads strung across the rooms in which he made them fly. He could make no more sense out of this conclusion than could his critics. But he trusted experimentally demonstrated facts sufficiently to be convinced of the correctness of his findings, even though he could not fit them into a satisfactory logical framework. This situation may arise from time to time in any branch of science, and often it means that some important new principle is just beyond our grasp. When facts fail to fit into our theories, there is usually a need to modify the theories.

Is there any reason to suppose that scientific history has just recently come to an end? Almost certainly not, and this inevitably means that new and totally unexpected discoveries are going to be made in the future. The example of Spallanzani and the acoustic orientation of bats can remind us of several important points. First the most rewarding discoveries may be awaiting us in what seem at first sight the most unlikely places. Second accepted theories explaining a phenomenon have often proved in the past to be mistaken. There is always room for constructive questioning of even the most well established theories. Who knows what current beliefs may be shown to be as much in need of revision as the nineteenth-century view that bats felt their way through dark caves by some sense of touch residing in their wings?

CHAPTER 2

Echoes as Messengers

Since bats and porpoises learn so much by listening to echoes, it is important to examine the properties of sound waves that make them such useful messengers. Before sounds or other types of wave motion can tell us anything at all, they must *interact* with something–the surface of the earth, the walls of a house, a human larynx, or the intricate mechanism of an ear that listens. Only by its doing something to some piece of matter, directly or indirectly, can wave motion be detected in the first place. Try to imagine a kind of radiation which penetrates whatever may stand in its way, traveling on and on without being changed, distorted, or deviated in its direction of travel. How could we learn that such rays even existed? High-energy cosmic rays and the subatomic particles called *neutrinos* have only the very slightest effect on matter under ordinary conditions, and, therefore, they were most difficult to discover and still are almost impossible to measure with any precision. Radio waves from natural sources have always existed at low levels of intensity and they penetrated the bodies of our ancestors just as they do our own. But only in very recent times have men observed the interactions of radio waves with appropriate detecting instruments and thus learned of their existence. Suppose that everything in the world were suddenly made perfectly transparent and, furthermore, that nothing gave off light or caused it to change direction in passing from one material to another. In such a world one might as well be blind. Even though you possessed the only sense organ or detecting instrument capable of receiving a type of radiation that penetrated everything else in the universe, such special powers would be of little use. Because light and sound do interact with matter around us, they are types of radiation for which sensitive detectors are useful. This is why animals and men have come to possess such effective eyes and ears.

The Nature of Sound Waves

Wave motion can conveniently be thought about in pure and continuous form: a sound having a single frequency, for instance 2000 sound waves or cycles per second, or light of a pure spectral color, for instance the D line of the sodium arc having a frequency of 5.1×10^{14} c.p.s. (51,000,000,000,000 c.p.s.). Such continuous waves may be described quite accurately for most purposes by a graph in which the size or *amplitude* of the wave motion is plotted on one axis and *time* on the other axis. For sound of a single frequency or a single spectral color such graphs are smoothly undulating lines called *sine* waves. A sine wave is the graph you would draw if you plotted the vertical motion of the hand of a clock as a function of time. Suppose you tied a string to the end of the hour hand of a wall clock, such as the one in almost any schoolroom, and tied a light weight to the other end of the string (Fig. 2). At nine o'clock

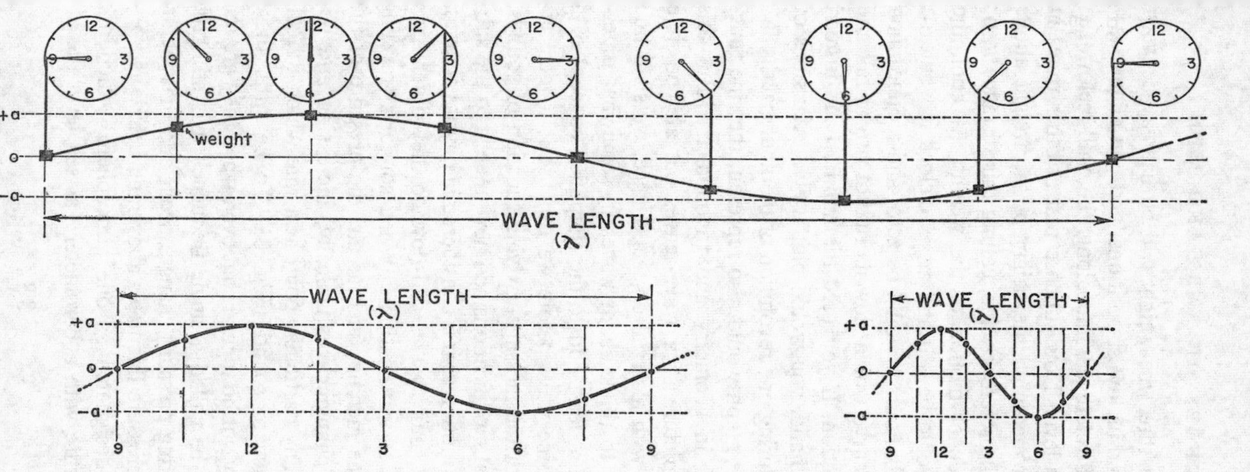

Fig. 2. Oscillations of many different objects such as a pendulum or these clock hands plotted on a graph describe a sine curve, or the smooth increase and decrease of distance, or amplitude with respect to time. The two bottom curves show the same amplitudes as the large curve but on two different time scales.

and again at three the weight will be halfway between its highest and its lowest positions, and you might draw a horizontal reference line along the wall below the clock at this level. Now suppose that at other times in the day you measured the height of the weight above and below the reference line, calling this distance a, or the amplitude of motion of the weight. At noon the amplitude would be $+a$ and at six o'clock it would be $-a$. Every six hours a would be zero, and around noon and six the curve would slow its rate of rise or fall and reverse direction. If you used the minute hand instead of the hour hand, you would plot twelve excursions of the weight during one revolution of the hour hand.

This same graph would also represent the sine function studied in geometry and trigonometry. But this convenient picture of a wave leaves out any possible interactions with material objects. Hence, we shall find it necessary to think about waves in somewhat different ways or at least add to the simplified concept of a continuous sine wave before we can use it to deal effectively with the message-carrying function of sounds. These special modifications add new interest to the subject of wave motion as it is considered in physics courses.

What are sound waves and how do they differ from other kinds of wave motion? When sound is traveling through some medium such as air, the pressure of the medium is changing rhythmically, increasing and decreasing at any particular point at a rate which we call the frequency of sound (Fig. 3). To be sure, these changes may not be regular, but even when they are too irregular to be called a single frequency it is still true that alternating pressure changes occur and that the atmospheric pressure fluctuates above and below its average value, designated as one atmosphere, which one would measure with a barometer (at sea level the at-

nosphere exerts the same pressure as does a 76-centi-
neter column of mercury). Furthermore, these regions of slightly higher or lower pressure travel through
he air, so that the zone of higher pressure which at
one moment is passing a particular point will later
e found some distance away. These pressure changes
re much smaller than most people realize; for ex-

Fig. 3. If you could photograph the molecules of air around a source of sound, you would find some molecules grouped closely and others loosely. There is a high pressure in the close-packed areas and a lower pressure elsewhere. A graph of this variation in pressure is a sine curve.

ample, a loud shout varies the air pressure by about 0.00001 to 0.0001 atmosphere, and the faintest sound that can be heard by a normal human listener has pressure variations of about 2×10^{-10} (2/10,000,000,000) atmosphere.

People used to question the existence of sound in the absence of a human listener. It was debated whether there was any sound from a waterfall in the wilderness when no one was there to hear it. This sort of question ceases to be of much importance once one distinguishes between the physical phenomenon of sound waves, pressure changes which travel through the air, and the subjective sensation of hearing a sound. The latter, of course, requires a listener, although an animal would do as well as a human being. But unless one believes that the waterfall and the air around it have wholly different properties when no man is present, it is beyond question that the physical sound waves are, in fact, generated as long as the water is falling.

Sound waves travel in liquids and solids as well as in gases such as air, and while most of the time we will be dealing with sound in air, we should bear in mind that sound waves (that is, moving pressure changes) also travel through the depths of the ocean or the hardest steel. There is, however, one great limitation to the travel of sound waves. They must have something to travel through and they are barred forever from empty space or from a perfect vacuum. Pressure results from the collisions of molecules with one another and with whatever surfaces form the boundaries of a gas, liquid, or solid. Sound can travel at appreciable intensities only where appreciable pressures exist, and this means where molecules are close enough together to collide with each other reasonably often.

The next important fact about sound waves is their

velocity of motion. Once started, they move through a given medium at a constant rate under any particular set of conditions. They usually become weaker and weaker as they progress, and eventually die out. But as long as they are detectable at all their velocity remains the same. Nor does the velocity vary with the frequency of sound. This means that when a sound contains more than one frequency (that is, the waves have more complicated shapes than simple sine curves), the different parts of the complex sound wave move together without one component lagging or gaining on the others. The actual speed of sound depends primarily upon the medium where the sound waves travel, but temperature and other factors affect it slightly. For example, in air at 20° C sound travels 344 meters per second (about 1130 feet/sec), and in sea water at 0° C its velocity is about 1550 meters/sec (or 4700 feet/sec). While these distances are fairly large, they are, of course, far less than the 3×10^8 meters (or 186,000 miles) covered in one second by light and radio waves. Hundreds or thousands of meters are less convenient to think about than shorter distances more comparable to our own dimensions. Consequently it will often be convenient to specify the velocity of sound in terms of distance traveled in 1 millisecond, or thousandth of a second; 344 meters/sec is 34.4 centimeters, or about one foot, per millisecond, a helpful figure to keep in mind when dealing with sounds of very short duration.

Another important property of a sound is its wave length or wave lengths. Wave length is the distance between successive zones of maximum or minimum pressures as the wave travels along. Since the velocity of sound is constant, the waves, which cover 344 meters in 1 second, may either be numerous and short or few in number and longer in wave length. If the waves are short, there are more of them in a given distance and more reach a given point in any particular interval of time, which is another way of saying they have a higher frequency. Expressed as a simple equation, velocity equals frequency times wave length ($v = f \times \lambda$). Or since the velocity is always the same under a given set of conditions, the wave length varies inversely as the frequency. A sound wave having a frequency of 344 waves or cycles per second has a wave length of approximately 1 meter; 1376 c.p.s. has a wave length of 0.25 meter, and a wave length of 2 centimeters (0.02 meter) corresponds to a frequency of $344 \div 0.02$, or 17,200 cycles per second. High frequencies are often expressed in kilocycles (thousands of cycles) per second, abbreviated kc. A sound lasting 1 second, whatever its frequency may be, extends 344 meters from start to end as it travels through the air. A click lasting only 1/100th second is 3.4 meters from front to back. And a sentence which takes 10 seconds to utter would extend 3440 meters (more than two miles) from the speaker's mouth if his voice were strong enough to carry that far. Assuming that the atmosphere is dense enough to carry sound waves up to an altitude of only 30,000 meters and your voice loud enough, it is amusing to estimate how long a sound would have to last in order to make a continuous series of sound waves from your mouth up to 30,000 meters. It would be 30,000/344 or about 87 seconds, or 1.5 minutes, roughly the time it would take you to read aloud half a page from a book.

The interactions of sound waves with ourselves and the objects around us are less obvious than those involving light. For example, almost every solid object casts some sort of shadow if exposed to light shining from one direction. But most familiar sounds can be heard with little change if the same shadow-casting object is

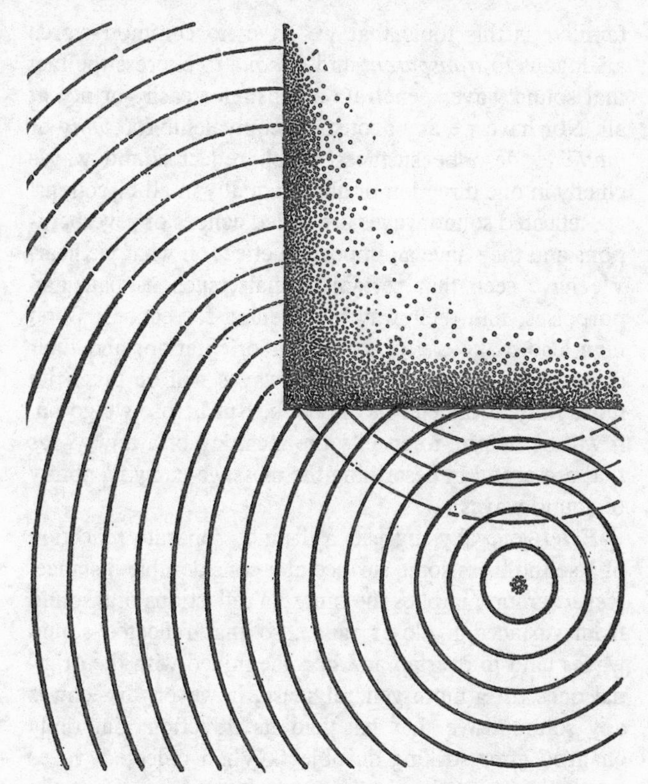

Fig. 4. Sound does not cast sharp shadows, but it does go around corners as well as being reflected back from solid objects.

placed between the sound source and the listener's ear. Due to greater wave lengths sound goes around corners far more than light. Test this by having a friend hum or whistle from behind a large tree trunk (Fig. 4). Even though sounds can be reduced in loudness by walls and other barriers, we seldom think about the degree to which they are blocked, transmitted, or reflected. So unfamiliar is this topic that we have no common words analogous to *transparent* and *opaque* to express the fact that sound waves penetrate a substance easily or not at all. Nor have we any acoustical equivalents for *shiny* or *matte* to describe surfaces which reflect sound waves chiefly in one direction or about equally in all directions.

Reflected sound waves are called echoes or reverberations and they have an important effect on what we hear. We have seen that certain animals, such as bats and porpoises, find their way by listening for echoes. Blind men also make use of sound for orientation, and their dependence on reflected sound waves will be taken up more fully at the end of the book. But before we go on, it will be helpful to specify the meaning of a few words that are useful in describing the message-carrying ability of sound waves.

Echo generally suggests a distinct, separate reflection of a sound from some surface at a considerable distance. *Reverberation* implies the multiple reflections of a sound from surfaces at closer range, so that reflected sound waves tend to overlap and become mixed with the original ones. In a more general sense, however, an echo is any sound wave that has had its direction materially changed after striking an object. When reflected waves travel through the same space as later waves from the same sound source, they interact and either increase or decrease the previous level of air pressure. If the pressure at a given point at a given time is increased by the presence of the echo waves, we say *constructive interference* or reinforcement has occurred; if the sound pressure is reduced from what it would have been without the reflected waves, we speak of *destructive interference* or cancellation. These terms have just the same meaning for sound waves as for light.

It is important to appreciate the relationship between

the velocity of sound, on the one hand, and the distinction between reverberations and echoes on the other. In air, where we do most of our listening, a sound lasting one second extends 344 meters through the air, and only if it is reflected from an object more than half that distance away (172 meters) will a listener close to the source receive an echo which begins after the original sound has ended. Several syllables can be uttered in 1 second—"one thousand one," for instance—and with a little effort a short syllable such as *de* can be repeated as rapidly as five times per second. If one spoke a single short syllable lasting 0.2 second, an echo would be separated from the outgoing sound even though the reflecting surface was only slightly more than 34 meters (172 × 0.2) away. It is not often that we hear echoes clearly separated in time from the original sounds that created them. This is partly because we seldom deal with single sounds as short as 0.2 second, or reflecting surfaces as distant as 34 meters, and also because our ears do not distinguish two sounds as separate unless there is a fraction of a second of quiet between them. Even when two sounds are so close together in time that they seem to be single, the combination usually sounds different from either of its two parts if they are heard alone. Two clicks that follow each other too closely to be heard as a double click sound duller than either one all by itself. Or, if closer still, the pair of clicks may simply sound louder than one alone.

Echoes We Seldom Notice

The echoes that usually follow every word we speak add to its quality and impact even though we are not aware of the reverberations as separate and distinct. This can be illustrated by simple experiments in which some constant sound source is carried in and out of doors. A talkative companion might be one's first choice for a test source of sound, but he will almost certainly change the loudness of the conversation on moving from a closed room to the open air. A portable radio is better, provided that the building does not contain enough metal to act as a shield for radio waves. First one might choose an ordinary frame house for the experiment and set the volume control of the radio to a level which produces comfortably loud speech or music as the set rests on the ground. Carrying the same radio into a small room makes it sound much louder. Not only do the sound waves reflected from the walls add to the total acoustic energy reaching our ears, but also the announcer's voice will seem to change its quality because the room has selective effects on different frequencies of sound.

Of course this experiment is a crude one, complicated by many pitfalls. Perhaps there were distracting noises on the street, or at one time you may have stood closer to the loudspeaker. Perhaps the announcer happened to talk louder during the time you had the set indoors. A better experiment might involve some more constant source—a whistle, typewriter, alarm clock, or other noise-making machine, a baby's rattle or the louder kind made for use on New Year's Eve. Best of all, in many ways, is to use a tape recorder which can be carried back and forth, indoors or outdoors. In this way you can use the same sample of speech or music or perhaps make up a tape recording in which the same sequence is repeated often enough so that you can listen to it repeatedly indoors and out. If you are still skeptical, and you should be, you may wonder whether anything changes in you, the listener, as you move back and forth. Does your hearing become less sensitive when you are in the open air? Many careful experiments have shown that this is not so in ordinary circumstances. Furthermore, we can make objective measurements of sound intensity in the two places with a microphone attached to a sensitive voltmeter. Such measurements confirm our impression that the same source of a continuous sound such as speech or music does produce a higher sound level indoors.

Let us pursue the matter a little further and assume that a tape recorder is available for experiments of this type–perhaps you can borrow one from a friend or your school. It will be more useful if you have a long extension cord, perhaps 50 feet in length, so that the instrument can be operated well away from the building as well as indoors. What sorts of sounds shall we compare in the two situations in order to learn as much as we can about the effects of echoes on how sounds sound with and without echoes and reverberations? Speech and music are excellent to get a better general understanding of these effects. But no two passages will have the same assemblage of sound waves, and it will be difficult to compare the quality of the different notes, words, and syllables in the same recording when heard indoors and out. With the microphone of your tape recorder you can record a sustained vocal note or one from any musical instrument. It is difficult to make a recording which is really continuous and does not fluctuate in loudness. But the best solution is to splice the tape into a continuous closed loop long enough to pass around both reels so that the machine plays the same sample over and over again.

This experiment will immediately demonstrate one important effect of echoes in a room. If a shrill, high-frequency note is maintained at a constant level in an ordinary room and if one listens to it carefully while moving slowly across the room, its loudness will rise and fall at regular intervals of distance. It is of particular interest to observe this effect while moving slowly near the middle of a room with the tape recorder at one end of the room playing a note that is two or three octaves above middle C. The comparison may be easier if one ear is covered so that the tone is heard entirely through the other. Listening in this way, one can usually hear clearly the waxing and waning of the sound level and you can, with care, estimate the distance from one loud spot to the next. A meter stick hanging horizontally at about eye level may make it easier to judge the distance through which the ear must move in order to pass from one point of maximum loudness to the next.

Having observed these fluctuations in the level of our recorded tone within a closed room, you repeat the same experiment out of doors. Not only will the tone sound fainter but the fluctuations will largely disappear; the loudness will fall off gradually as one walks away from the loudspeaker. Such a simple experiment as this will demonstrate that reflected sound waves from the walls of the room are interacting with those coming straight from the tape recorder and that at some places there is constructive interference producing maximum sound levels, while elsewhere there is destructive interference causing zones of relative quiet. The distance between points of maximum loudness will be *one half wave length,* because changes in either direction from the mean atmospheric pressure are what stimulate our ears. C_2, the second C above middle C, is a convenient tone to use; it has a frequency of 1024 c.p.s. and a wave length of approximately 30 centimeters. On the other hand, at a lower frequency, such as 100 c.p.s., the wave length will equal or exceed the dimensions of the room ($\lambda = \frac{v}{f} = \frac{344}{100} = 3.4$ meters), and at 10 kc or higher the successive maxima and minima ($\lambda = \frac{344}{10{,}000} = 0.034$ meters or 3.4 centimeters) will be too close together for easy detection. Notes from musical instruments have so many frequencies, or harmonics, each giving its own maxima and minima at its own wave length, that it will be difficult to distinguish the loud and quiet spots for each frequency. Hence, the purer the note the more obvious the effect. You will find the flute more satisfactory because of its purer tone than a piano or violin.

These maxima and minima are called *standing waves.* A loud spot is the point where sound waves reflected from the walls add to others arriving directly from the loudspeaker. If several parts of the walls all send strong reflections to the same spot, these various echoes are likely to arrive at different times and fail to reinforce each other as strongly as they would if arriving at the same time. In some rooms of irregular shape the standing waves may thus be inconspicuous, but most rooms are regular enough and have sufficiently reflective walls so that at least in the middle of the room the standing-wave pattern is noticeable. If you have an opportunity to experiment with a ripple tank in which surface waves on water are generated to illustrate the various phenomena of wave motion, you will find that the frequency of the vibrating object producing the waves has to be adjusted rather carefully to obtain pronounced standing waves. Otherwise the water's surface may show only a shifting and confusing mess of wavelets chasing each other back and forth without apparent order. If the tank is not a simple shape, such as a rectangle, then the standing-wave patterns are either very complicated or are limited to a few areas where reflected waves do manage to reinforce those arriving directly from their source.

Suppose we try to set up standing waves in a room by

generating not a single frequency but a sound containing many different frequencies. Speech and music answer this description, but the different frequencies change rapidly with time, so the effects are complicated. Still, it is true that even though we do not ordinarily notice standing waves of speech or music, in some very large rooms there may be "dead spots" where interference between the direct and reflected sound makes listening very difficult and unpleasant. Indeed, there is a whole science of architectural acoustics devoted to minimizing such "dead spots" and to controlling the echoes from the walls of auditoria so that speech and music are carried as faithfully as possible to all parts of the hall.

A simple experiment with our tape recorder in an ordinary room can demonstrate the effects of having many frequencies present at the same time. A loud hiss made vocally into the microphone will, when played back, fill the room with a still louder hiss. But you will probably have great difficulty in hearing standing waves. The same experiment can sometimes be performed by turning up the volume control of a radio or record player until you hear a hissing sound that incidentally stems from the random motions of molecules in some part of the electronic circuit. It has a wide range or band of frequencies, as does a vocal hiss, and all are about equally loud. So many different wave lengths are present that even though each one tends to set up standing waves at its own wave length, all the others have equally strong tendencies to establish loud spots separated by *their* wave lengths. The result is that the over-all level of the sound is much the same from point to point within the room. To obtain clear standing waves there must be only one or a very few wave lengths prominent in the sound that fills the room.

Perhaps when you are listening for standing waves

someone else may walk into the room. Often this will cause a shift in the positions of the maxima and minima even though the room is fairly large. This is a more complicated type of interaction in which the exact location of greatest interference is influenced by all sorts of objects that add reflected sound waves to those arriving directly from the tape recorder. Because of these changes the standing-wave patterns could be used to tell us that someone had entered the room. Usually we have much easier ways of knowing this, but there are circumstances where changes in standing-wave patterns have been put to use to detect small changes in the position of objects in a room. One type of burglar alarm operates on this principle. Suppose you were walking about blindfolded in the same room. The standing-wave pattern would at least inform you that you were in a room and not out of doors where nothing was reflecting enough sound to set up standing waves. It could also tell you when something else moved into the room, provided you were standing still and noticed the shift in the standing waves.

These may seem to be trivial examples, but blind men do learn to pay attention to many aspects of the sound fields in which they live and in this way learn much about what goes on around them. Remember, too, that these examples have been selected for their simplicity, and from such crude beginnings we can go on to much more difficult questions that can be answered by carrying these experiments further. This is in essence to use sound waves as *tools* or "sense extenders" for exploring one's surroundings. Crude tools used with little skill yield only crude information. But, as we already have seen, even such small animals as bats have become expert at using sound waves as tools of this sort to learn rather complicated facts about what goes on around them. They have come to do this in the long course of their evolutionary history because they live and move under conditions where sound is a convenient or perhaps the only available means for maintaining their orientation.

Telling whether you are indoors or out on the street by listening to a tape recording of a shrill and monotonous tone may seem a clumsy way to accomplish the obvious. But transpose the situation to a man lost in a pitch-black cave and unable to use a light of any kind. Sound waves would be one of the most useful means, if not the only means, at his disposal to learn about those parts of the cave beyond the direct reach of his outstretched hands and feet. Bats do not feel their way; they fly rapidly through complex and tortuous passages of a cave, dodging stalactites and other bats without accidents of any kind, and, as I shall explain later, this is one of the less difficult of the many tasks these little animals accomplish by means of sound waves.

In pursuing these matters further it will be best to return from time to time to the simple experiments with audible sounds such as those we have just conducted. In this way you may have firsthand experience to confirm and support the concepts and theories about which you read. For many purposes the ripple tank used in physics courses provides more convenient types of waves with which the same phenomena can equally well be visualized. This is basically because surface waves on water travel slowly enough for you to watch them directly. Furthermore, their velocity varies with the depth of the water, and they can be caused to bend by installing shallow "sandbars" or "reefs" in the ripple tank. The same ripple tank can also be used to study echoes which are closely analogous to those that cause standing waves of sound and to those used by bats or men to find their way about in situations where light is not available.

Water Waves and Surface Echoes

There are many and detailed parallels between water waves and sound waves in air or, for that matter, light waves; but aside from their serving as slow-motion models, we are likely to think of surface waves on water as of little interest and certainly as wholly devoid of the ability to carry information. Who would think of trying to signal back and forth across the ocean by means of water waves? They die out too soon and are too easily confused with the natural waves from winds or water currents. A leaf that falls to the surface of a quiet pond may produce a few ripples, but how could one hope to detect this event a hundred feet away? Yet from their very similarity to sound or light we might expect the water waves we study in the physics laboratory to have some message-carrying function. Such cases can be found if we look for them in nature and, in this instance, the search leads to the so-called whirligig beetle which bridges the gap between the ripple tank and the most complicated radar installations.

Whirligig beetles are common inhabitants of small ponds and quiet streams. While these aquatic insects often dive and swim below the surface, they are usually noticed most easily when darting about on the surface film of the water. They are light enough in weight so that they are supported by the surface tension of the water–largely because of their fringe of hairs covered with a thin film of waxy material that does not readily become wetted. This ability to support themselves on water could easily lead us into a digression about surface tension and why water is a uniquely suitable liquid for the flotation of water beetles. But this is a subject which is covered well in the Science Study Series book *Soap Bubbles.*

More pertinent is the fact that the water beetles make use of surface waves to keep themselves posted about the proximity of the water's edge. They have eyes and use them under many conditions, but at night or when vision is prevented by laboratory experiments performed in darkness they still manage quite skillfully to avoid collisions with the edge of an aquarium and with each other. A German biologist named Friedrich Eggers

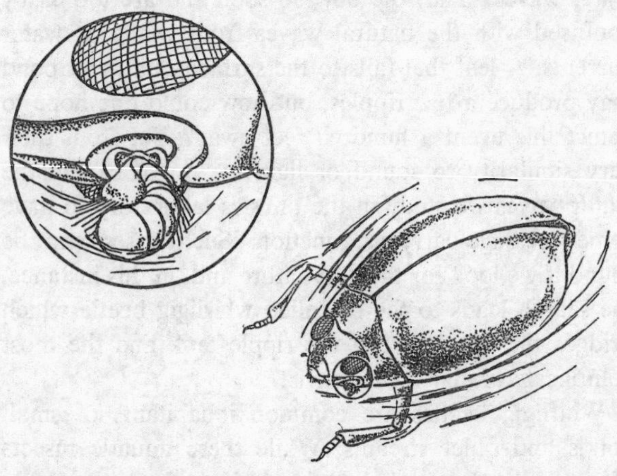

Fig. 5. A whirligig beetle whose other legs lie beneath its body is able to sense water waves and their echoes with the two specialized antennae which protrude from the head and float on the water. It is also interesting to note that this beetle has four compound eyes, two above the water and two below.

studied these beetles with great care in the 1920s. Unlike those of most insects, their antennae, or feelers are shaped in an especially suitable way to float on the surface film of the water. The numerous hairs all arranged parallel to each other are at just the correct angle so that they float in the surface film. But more specialized still are the hairs located on one particular joint of each antenna, the second from the base. These specialized hairs are more than flotation devices; at the base are sensitive nerves that are stimulated by the most minute movements of the hairs relative to the remainder of the beetle. Eggers surmised from the microscopic structure of these hairs and nerves (see Fig. 5) that they were used to detect motion of the water surface, and he therefore experimented with them directly. In some beetles he damaged the second segments of the antennae, cut off the hairs on this portion, or damaged only the nerves leading from the bases of these hairs into the central nervous system of the insect. When these water beetles were placed on the surface of an aquarium in the dark, they acted as bewildered as a bird fluttering against a windowpane and collided at random with the walls.

Other experiments have shown that the sense organs of insects can respond to very weak vibrations. A movement of as little as 4×10^{-9} centimeter is detected by the sensory nerves attached to fine hairs on the surface of some insects which are generally similar in structure to the whirligig water beetles. There is thus no reason to be amazed that water beetles can feel the surface waves generated by their own swimming or walking movements. What is amazing is their ability to discriminate the jiggling that results from reflected waves from all the other vibrations that must be affecting the same hairs and the same sensory nerves. This is a problem which the beetles may avoid to a considerable extent by their habit of swimming intermittently, with frequent pauses during which they may perhaps be feeling the "reverberations" of the water waves their swimming has generated a fraction of a second earlier. But the navigation of water beetles has not been studied since Eggers' day, and it is typical of the opportunities that await patient and ingenious students of biophysics. In the following chapters I shall describe in more detail better known examples of animals' and men's learning a great deal by listening for echoes, and it will become apparent that living sense organs and brains detect echoes that seem on first thought far too faint to be of any possible use. The phenomenon is basically one of discrimination, or sifting out faint but important echoes from much stronger waves of the same type which are not relevant for the purposes of the particular animal. Living nervous systems are superior to artificial machines in making a wide variety of fine discriminations, and the next chapter describes experiments you can perform yourself to show how the human ear and brain discriminate among various types of sounds including echoes.

CHAPTER 3

Airborne Echoes of Audible Sounds

The word "echo" suggests a quiet country scene where a steep cliff or hillside looms up hundreds of feet away. A shout or a gunshot suddenly breaks the silence, and there follows a repetition of the sound, fainter than the original. Knowing the velocity of sound, we could determine our distance from the hillside if we accurately measured the interval of time from the onset of the outgoing sound to the arrival of the first echo. This can be done with a stop watch, provided that the hill is large enough and distant enough so that a clearly audible echo will return after some seconds. If the hill is too close, the time interval will be too short for easy and accurate measurement; if it is too far away, the echo may not be audible at all. Often there are too many hills producing multiple echoes, and if the first of these overlaps the end of the outgoing sound or there are reverberations from objects in our immediate vicinity, then the accurate measurement becomes difficult. Nor is it always easy to decide just which hill is sending back the echo; in fact, the easiest procedure often is to time the echo and then scrutinize a large-scale map in search of a steep hillside at the correct distance. And there are almost always other sounds to compete for our attention. Thus obvious echoes have come to seem rather special sounds to be heard only in the most favorable circumstances.

One situation where echoes have been put to practical use is aboard boats in foggy coastal waters. Usually it is quiet in a fog and, aside from the boat itself, no echoing surface interrupts until the shore is reached. Often fishermen who find themselves in foggy waters and think that steep shore lines or cliffs may be within a mile or so produce a clear echo by making a short, loud sound. Sometimes this is a blast of a horn or whistle, required by law in any case to signal their presence to other boats, or the probing signal may be simply a shout. Some fishermen say they can even hear echoes from channel-marker buoys (about three feet in diameter) at several hundred feet. The usefulness of this method of navigation is often limited by the lack of adequate echoing targets in the air above the actual underwater hazards. Rocks need not reach the surface to be dangerous, and most shore lines are too gentle to provide reliable echoes.

Modern instruments have largely supplanted airborne sound by transposing the same basic process into the water itself. Sound waves are broadcast from the boat's hull, and echoes of underwater sound from the bottom or from shoals ahead of the boat are recorded by instruments. Such devices for echolocation under water are called *echo sounders* or *fathometers*—the more refined models can even detect schools of fish. All these methods have in common the emission of a probing sound, the detection of echoes, and, most important, the discerning of the distance and direction of the object that returns the echo.

The Acoustics of Clicks and Echoes

Because almost every object reflects sound to an appreciable degree, it is very rare for any sound to reach our ears without embellishment by echoes. Why then are the echoes so rarely noticed? Seldom do they occur separately; that is, they rarely arrive at a different time from the sound that produced them. Usually they and the original sound are mixed, and we ordinarily fail to discriminate between the two classes of sound waves. The simple experiments with a portable radio or tape recorder suggested in the previous chapter demonstrated that echoes were present indoors and that they could make a tone or a noise sound different. The loudness is increased by the addition of strong echoes from the walls of a room and by standing waves that may be audible when continuous pure tones are present indoors. But the important point is that special experiments were necessary to convince us that echoes really are so common a part of the most familiar sounds. One major reason echoes escape our notice so completely is the relatively long duration of most sounds compared to the time they require to bounce back in our customary places of living and listening. Even on the shore of a mountain lake we are not likely to notice echoes of the songs we may sing about a campfire, for they will usually be masked by the notes that follow. Only when the song comes to an abrupt ending will the echoes from the hills intrude upon our consciousness. The masking of echoes by the continuing sound explains much of our inability to notice them in ordinary circumstances.

But all sounds come to an end, eventually at least, and there are always pauses or brief intervals of silence. Why don't we hear the echoes then? Suppose we try to investigate the physics of this question by setting up a sensitive microphone to convert the energy of sound waves into electric voltages. Suppose further that we have connected this microphone to an instrument such as a cathode-ray oscilloscope, which draws a visible graph of the sound waves almost instantaneously. A cathode-ray oscilloscope is the forerunner of your television set. Inside the picture tube a spot of light is created, and one electric circuit moves this spot horizontally and again and again at a uniform rate from left to right while another moves it up and down. In this application the up-and-down movement is produced by the amplified voltage from the microphone. On the picture screen the combined horizontal and vertical motion literally draws a graph of sound pressure against time.

With such a machine we can watch the behavior of the sound waves while we utter them. If we suddenly stop talking, the movement of the spot of light on the picture tube may seem to stop at the same instant. But if one looks closely, and if the instrument is set up in a large hall, one can easily see that the oscilloscope continues briefly to draw a diminishing graph of the sound waves that are still traveling back and forth past the microphone from wall to wall. Because sound waves travel about 344 meters per second, and because less than 100 per cent of the sound energy is reflected back from each contact with the walls or floor, and finally because sound waves are reduced slowly by their frictional effects on the molecules of the air, the continuing echoes are appreciable for only a fraction of a second. But they are there, and our eyes can see them on the oscilloscope screen even when our ears do seem not to hear them.

With instruments we can improve upon the ability of our eyes to judge how fast the sound level declines and how long it is detectable at all. One of the simplest methods is to photograph the moving spot on the oscilloscope screen with a camera in which the film moves at a constant rate. While the spot moves up and down as the sound waves strike the microphone, the motion of the film draws a graph of sound pressure on the vertical axis against time on the horizontal axis. The resulting graphic picture of sound waves makes it easy to see the echoes which continue to arrive at the microphone a

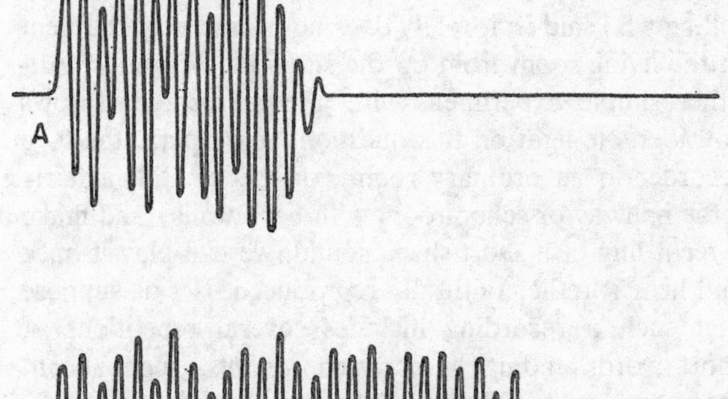

Fig. 6. A graph of the sound pressure in a very short word without any echo is shown in A, and the same word with echoes is shown in B. Note the similarity of the early waves in A and B, and a difference as the echo returns before the original word has ended.

good fraction of a second after the end of the sound that came directly from a speaker's mouth. Such photographs also show clearly the greater magnitude of the echoes that follow the same word spoken indoors rather than out. An example of this comparison is seen in Fig. 6, but even here where the word was a short one the echoes began to mix with the original sound waves long before the end of the word.

Despite all these differences in the photographic portrait, the same word spoken in these two situations sounds about the same. Again the amazing fact is that all these special procedures are necessary to convince us that the two sets of sound waves are *not* exactly the same. We have no difficulty recognizing the word or in telling who said it; it really does not sound very different in the living room from on the sidewalk. Why not? Another simple experiment with a tape recorder throws considerable light on this question. If we place the tape recorder in an ordinary room (or, better still, a fairly large hallway or schoolroom with hard walls) and make a recording of a short sharp sound, we can play it back and hear it rather faithfully reproduced. Let us suppose that such a recording includes several repetitions of short words ending in hard consonants, such as *bit, took, sud,* or *leg*. Sharp clicks such as one can make by snapping together a pair of large scissors or pliers may also be used; and if one wishes a good excuse for it, a cap-pistol report is excellent for this experiment. In any event each recorded sound should be separated from the next by a few seconds of quiet.

When such a tape recording has been made, *play it backward.* That is, interchange the two reels so that the tape moves back end first when the machine is playing back the recording. What used to be the take-up reel becomes the reel from which the tape is unwound and vice versa. On full track recorders it is only necessary to turn the two reels upside down when interchanging them, so that the same side of the tape will pass next to the recording head. Newer stereo machines use only a narrow part of the tape when a given recording is made, and when played back in the reverse direction, this part will not pass by the pick-up head. In this case the reversed tape can sometimes be played backward by reversing its surface orientation. This reduces the level of the sound, but the volume control can usually be turned up to compensate for this loss, and the experiment can still be performed, though less well than with tape which is recorded across its full width.

When the tape is played backward, the echoes that followed the original word or click will of course precede it. Since they were hardly noticeable before, one would naturally expect them to be a faint prelude to the reversed sound. But the actual result is a startling increase in the apparent loudness of the echoes. A click that sounded very sharp in its original form, or when a tape recording of it is played back in the normal direction, now becomes a gradually rising hiss that culminates in the click. The click proper does not sound very different frontward or backward, but the reversed echoes are much more apparent. So much so that when one hears this demonstration it is difficult to believe that the instrument has not played some trick, that the whooossschk! is really the same sound as the sharp click that gave rise to it.

This reversed playback technique reveals the real magnitude of the echoes from various sounds, but it is more difficult to appreciate with reversed speech or music, which sounds very abnormal in other ways. Clicks or pistol shots are in themselves so short that they contain only a few irregular sound waves, which are not very different-sounding when played in either direction. This can be demonstrated by repeating the recording out of doors in a quiet area well away from any large building. The clicks will now be accompanied by only minor echoes from the ground or other small objects, such as trees or bushes. When played back in the reverse direction, they will sound far closer to the original than they did indoors. In short, this experiment shows the extent to which our sense of hearing de-emphasizes echoes. Sound waves which would be clearly audible if they existed in isolation are almost totally ignored if they happen to be part of an echo arriving a few tenths of a second after another sound. This goes far to explain why spoken words or other sounds do sound nearly the same when heard indoors with strong echoes from the walls or out of doors with few echoes or none. Of course there is a difference if one listens carefully for it, and, in addition to being louder, speech heard in a closed room has a "thicker" quality. The echoing sound of footsteps in a very large empty room is a common observation. Almost everyone has also noted the forlorn sounds of footsteps or conversation in a house emptied of its furniture and draperies. All these effects are caused by either the presence or absence of strong echoes.

The mechanism by which we suppress echoes is one of many subtle mysteries of the human ear and brain, and no one understands how it is accomplished. The suppression lasts only a small fraction of a second; indeed, it has been shown to be greatest immediately after the end of the direct sound and then to diminish gradually until after half a second or so another sound can be heard about as well as ever. An echo from a distant hillside arriving four or five seconds after the end of the outgoing sound is easy enough to hear if it is quiet where one is listening. But the same strength of echo would be inaudible if it arrived 1/10th second after its original was emitted. By playing a tape recording backward, we remove the echoes from the time interval when our suppressor mechanism is at work.

In trying to learn what echoes sound like, it is best to

use sounds of short duration simply because they are less likely to overlap and be wholly masked by their originals. The sounds of spoken syllables or clicking scissors are not as short as one would ideally like to use. Any sound shorter than about 1/10th second is usually called a click, and the shorter it is the sharper it sounds, provided it has a reasonably high energy level. The human voice cannot produce really short clicks, however, nor can any other ordinary sound source. An electric spark caused by the discharge of a condenser is a very sharp click, and the discharge of a condenser through a loudspeaker is nearly as sharp, provided that the electrical circuit involved does not resonate and prolong the vibration of the speaker diaphragm. A cheaper and more widely available source of sharp clicks is a common toy, the frog or cricket made of a thin strip of spring steel with a dent in the middle. This is clamped tightly to a holder at one end; the other end is free to be pushed back and forth in such a way that the strip is bent and unbent. When your finger bends the strip of steel, the dent is suddenly inverted to impart a very sudden and energetic push to the air as it snaps from concave to convex or vice versa. The result is a very loud and sharp click, painfully loud if generated close to the ear, possibly even damaging if it were to be repeated many times immediately in front of the ear opening.

The actual duration of the click varies from one model of toy to another, and it is affected by the size and shape of the holding device. In small clickers that I have tested the sound falls to 1/10th its initial maximum within about 10 milliseconds after the steel dent has snapped from one position to another. Recalling that the velocity of sound in air is approximately one foot per millisecond, you can calculate that a click lasting 10 milliseconds has a physical length of about 10 feet as it travels through the air. This means that echoes will begin to reach the listener after being reflected from a wall 5 feet away just as the last of the click leaves the device. If we had a clicker that gave out a 1-millisecond sound, this overlap between echo and original sound would cease at distances greater than 6 inches.

It is interesting to take such a clicker and listen for its echoes. Even the ordinary toys producing 10-millisecond clicks will add significantly to the knowledge we obtained with echoes from spoken words. In these experiments it will be important to maximize the audibility of the echoes while reducing the level of the outgoing sound which reaches our ears directly. Part of the echo-suppressing effect mentioned earlier is a very brief reduction in the sensitivity of our hearing for a fraction of a second after the arrival of a very large sound, and these clickers at close range are really very loud indeed. A good procedure is to hold a typical toy clicker with your two hands cupped around it and opened to form a forward facing horn so that the hands are between clicker and your ears. The outgoing click will still be plainly audible, but its main sound energy output will be directed straight ahead. All the striking effects I have described can be heard on reversed playback of such clicks. In making a tape recording for reversed playback, you should keep the microphone behind the cupped hands, too, so that it also will be better situated to receive the echoes than to receive the original emitted click. With this very short click we can also begin to hear echoes directly without any tape recorder or reversed playback.

One of these toy clickers held in the cupped hands can be used to good advantage out of doors. If the hands and clicker are pointed at a building 50 feet or so away, a clear and separate echo can easily be heard.

It can also be used to get distinct echoes from trees a foot in diameter, and other objects can be located in the same way. A good technique for a beginner is to sweep slowly back and forth with the clicker while operating it at a rate of one or two clicks per second. A few minutes of careful listening will show that much can be learned about objects of this general size, provided that they are at a sufficient distance to yield an echo which is clearly separate from the emitted click itself. Experience will show that echoes are most easily recognized when only one large echoing surface is within range. Several trees in a courtyard surrounded by large buildings give multiple echoes that only careful scanning can resolve.

Before very long your hands become cramped from the unnatural position in which they must be held in order both to operate the clicker and provide it with a horn. It is not difficult to mount the clicker in a small horn made of cardboard, light metal, or plastic. While a parabolic shape is perhaps ideal, a fairly deep cone will serve fairly well. The most important point is to provide a means of bending the dented sheet of steel back and forth without having any opening at the back of the horn through which the click can reach the user's ears directly at a high level of intensity. One device of this sort is shown in Fig. 7.

After you have learned to detect trees and houses by hearing their echoes, you will find it worth while to experiment with an easily recognized target such as a building. Keep moving closer as you click. If you find it difficult to be sure whether you are really hearing echoes, it may be helpful to try using the clicker while blindfolded or with your eyes closed. You will then be in much the same situation as a blind man trying to find his way about by means of echoes. Many blind people have

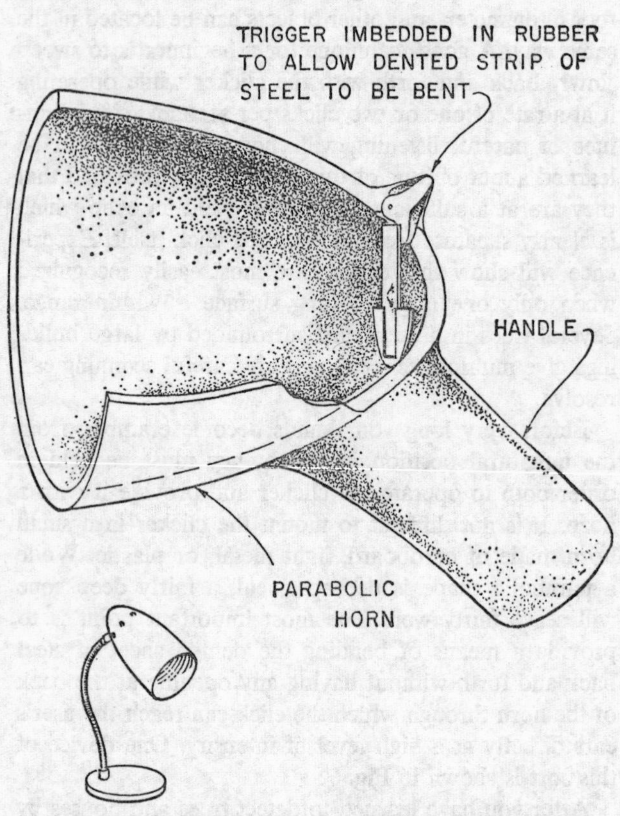

Fig. 7. A very satisfactory device for echo experiments can be made like this. The inside of the horn should be a paraboloid of revolution, and the clicker must be mounted at the focal point of the parabola. The Fiberglas and plastic boat- or car-patching materials laid on a plaster of Paris form make excellent horns, and so do the parabolic reflectors of certain desk lamps.

learned to do this with great skill and success. As you walk toward a building from 15–25 meters away, the echo of the clicker is at first clearly separated from the original click but gradually merges with it until there is only one sound as best you can tell. At this point you should turn in some other direction, where no large object will return echoes, and operate the clicker several times. The clicks will sound different, and if in doubt you can alternately point toward the building and then in some other direction. After this difference has been recognized, you can move in closer to the building, repeatedly clicking both toward it and away in non-echoing directions. It is surprising how close you can come and still be clearly aware of a difference in the sound of the clicker when it is pointed toward and away from the wall. At very close range, less than 10 feet for example, the difference will begin to be one of loudness; the echoes are of sufficient intensity that they add appreciably to the click with which they are fused. This is why the horn is so important to shield you from the direct sound; if the horn could be perfect, so that *all* the sound energy of the clicker traveled away from you, then the echoes would become unmistakable.

It is helpful to digress at this point into a little thought about the wave lengths of audible sounds and the relationship of these wave lengths to the practicable size for a horn to direct the click forward. It is a general property of wave motion that specular (that is, mirror-like) reflections can be obtained only from objects that are larger than one wave length. Water waves on the surface of a ripple tank or a bathtub can be reflected from the edges of the tank or tub or from objects several centimeters long. Such reflections obey the same rules as those that hold for light waves; for instance, the angle of reflection from a plane surface equals the angle of incidence. But quite different results are observed if the object reflecting the waves is only one wave length or less. Then one sees secondary waves which may be called echoes radiating in many directions from the small object. The strength of the echo waves in different directions varies in a complicated way, both with the shape of the object and particularly with its size, relative to the wave length. In fact, if the object is much smaller than one wave length, its shape makes almost no difference at all. Later on I shall describe some simple experiments with the clicker by which one can see how these same rules apply to audible sound waves. When the echoes travel in many directions from an object which itself is small compared to the wave length, they are often called *scattered* rather than reflected sound.

But we started this digression to consider how the wave length of the click would affect the usefulness of a horn to direct the sound straight forward. A horn is a special kind of acoustic mirror, and for this purpose we want one shaped so that sound waves generated somewhere inside will all be reflected from the horn's surfaces, reinforcing each other and coming out of the mouth as parallel wave fronts traveling in the same direction. If the sound is generated at a point, the most effective horn to concentrate the sound waves into one direction will be one with a parabolic shape. This means that if you cut the horn longitudinally, any section will be a parabola with the sound source at its focus. One of the geometrical properties of a parabola is that any line radiating from the focus will strike the surfaces of the parabola at such an angle that when reflected (at an angle equal to the angle of incidence) it will be parallel to the axis of the parabola.

This sounds rather complicated, but perhaps Fig. 8 will help to make it clear. Really this is a very familiar

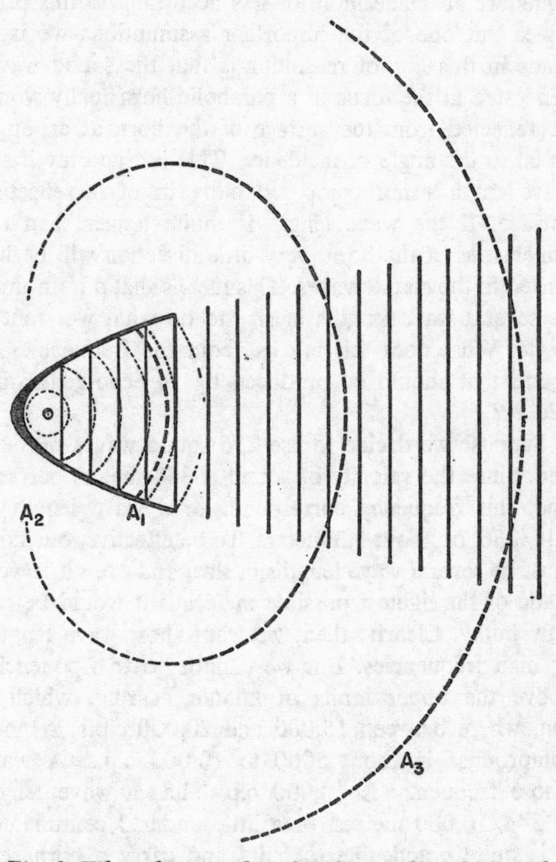

Fig. 8. When the wave length is larger than the mouth of the horn, as in the low-frequency sound waves A_1, A_2, and A_3, there is little or no focusing. But with a much smaller wave length a narrow beam of plane waves is produced.

story, for searchlights, flashlights, and automobile headlights are all made more or less according to this principle. But one of the important assumptions we have made in this line of reasoning is that the sound waves generated at the focus of a parabolic horn really would be reflected from the surface of the horn at an angle equal to the angle of incidence. This is true only if the wave length is short compared to the size of the reflecting surface. If the wave length is much longer than the dimensions of the horn, very little direction will be imparted to the sound waves. This means that a horn must be several wave lengths in size to do what we want it to do. What does this tell us about the frequencies of sound that should be produced by an echo-generating clicker?

Suppose we decide to use 256 sound waves per second. Since the velocity of sound is 344 meters per second, this frequency corresponds to a wave length of 344/256, or about 1.3 meters. To be effective, our horn must be several wave lengths in size, and even if it were made of the lightest possible materials it would be unduly bulky. Clearly, then, we want short wave lengths or high frequencies. But we cannot go to frequencies above the upper limits of human hearing, which is somewhere between 15,000 and 20,000 c.p.s. A good compromise is about 5000 to 10,000 c.p.s. A wave whose frequency is 10,000 c.p.s. has a wave length of 344/10,000 meters, or a little under 3 centimeters. It is quite practicable to build and carry a horn several centimeters in size, and if this were the only consideration we would choose the highest frequencies or shortest wave lengths that were easily audible. Bats use frequencies up to 130,000 c.p.s. with wave lengths down to 2.5 millimeters, and their tiny mouths or ears can concentrate these short sound waves quite effectively. The toy clicker produces a number of frequencies or wave lengths within each brief click, but it would require much more complicated click generators to produce an ideal click containing only a single frequency and a pulse short enough in duration to yield echoes distinctly separate from the original. Indeed, this consideration of separateness itself imposes limits on the possible frequencies. Several waves are necessary to establish a clear frequency, and if our sound is to last only 1 millisecond it can contain only 10 waves of 10,000 c.p.s., or 5 waves of 5000 c.p.s.

What I have been suggesting in these simple experiments with a clicker is to act as though you were blind and see what you can discover about the larger objects in your surroundings solely by means of echoes. Later on I shall discuss in more detail what blind people actually do and the success they have achieved as well as the limitations that seem to prevent echolocation from warning them about all the major obstacles that threaten their safe progress. But before turning to this direct application to a pressing problem of a large group of handicapped persons, we will find it helpful to consider certain physical properties of echoes that determine their strength and audibility. For this purpose we can make good use of both real echoes from a clicker and "echoes" in the ripple tank, which is so useful in the physics laboratory for the analysis of wave motion.

The Velocity of Sound Measured by Means of Echoes

As a beginning we may consider a simple method of determining the approximate velocity of sound by an extension of the already-mentioned procedure of timing the return of an echo from a distant hillside. If the distance to the hill is not known and if the travel time of the sound and its echo is a few seconds, a good stop watch (which can measure time to a tenth of a second) would allow us to determine the distance to the hill, if we assume that we know the velocity of sound. Or if we know the distance, we can use the same time measurement to estimate the velocity at which the sound waves travel. If the basic limit of accuracy in our time measurement is determined by the stop watch at 0.1 second, the uncertainty in our measurement of distance would be the distance over which sound travels in that interval of time, or approximately 34 meters. But this would be the round-trip distance, so that theoretically we could measure the distance to the hill with an accuracy of ± 17 meters. Another uncertainty is the human reaction time, the interval between the actual arrival of a sound and the pressing of the button on the stop watch. While this is an appreciable fraction, certainly more than 0.1 of a second, there is not likely to be a great difference between the first reaction time to the original sound and the reaction time in stopping the watch when one hears the echo; hence they will nearly cancel each other. Another error is likely to occur if the emitted sound and the echo build up gradually. If a half second is needed to reach maximum sound intensity, and if the echo is enough fainter so that only the peak value is audible, then we will probably find that the stop watch is pressed one reaction time after the very beginning of the outgoing sound, but not until one reaction time after the echo is nearly at its peak. This can easily cause an error of about 0.3 second unless a very sharp sound is used for the experiment.

A similar experiment can be performed with the clicker, provided it can be operated fairly rapidly. Suppose you stand 30 meters from a large building and point the clicker so that a distinct echo is heard. Since the sound travels 60 meters from clicker to building and back to your ears, this trip will require 60/344, or about 0.17 second. If you operate the clicker twice per second, you will hear an outgoing click at a time you may designate as zero, an echo at 0.17 second, a second emitted click at 0.50 second, a second echo at 0.67 second, etc. If we speed up our operation of the clicker, the second click will eventually come at 0.17 second and so will mask the echo. If we can operate the clicker with sufficient regularity, this fusion of echo with second click provides another way to measure distance–provided we know the velocity of sound. A mechanical device such as a metronome can control the rate of clicking more precisely, but with a little practice a good approximation can be achieved. One practical difficulty is that the click made by bending the strip of steel will usually be slightly louder or different in quality from that made when the strip is unbent. Thus successive clicks alternate in level or quality, and it is not always easy to maintain an even rhythm. But it can be done and, regardless of its practicability, it is worth while to understand this simple method for estimating distance by the rate of clicking necessary to cause each echo to fuse with the following click. One effective way to estimate the critical rate is to have someone else count the number of clicks in a 5- or 10-second period measured with a stop watch or the second hand of an ordinary watch.

The same clicker may also be used to demonstrate convincingly the concentration of echoes into certain directions when they have been reflected from surfaces of various sizes relative to the wave lengths in the click. Most toy clickers have a frequency range between 3 and 10 kilocycles, so that the most intense sound waves have wave lengths of a few centimeters. When such wave lengths strike the wall of a building, they are reflected almost exactly as light waves would be from a mirror. If the clicker is pointed directly at the wall, the echo will come straight back, but if the emitted sound strikes ob-

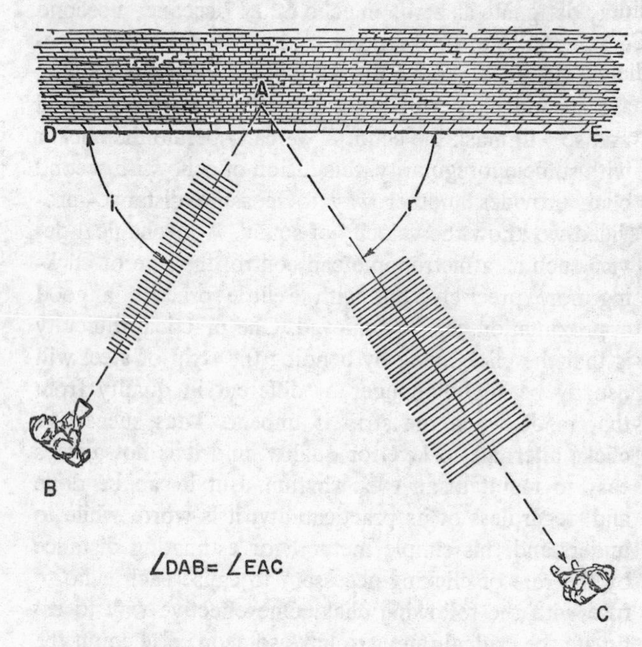

Fig. 9. The law of reflection describes the way in which sound reflects from a large flat surface. When making this experiment, observe the relative positions of the two boys.

liquely, the echoes will rebound away from the clicker, as indicated in Fig. 9. This is why it is so easy to locate a building by scanning with the clicker; the echo is far louder when the horn is pointed straight at the wall. Two people can co-operate in a simple experiment that demonstrates how these echoes behave. One should aim the clicker at the wall 20° to 30° to one side of a perpendicular from clicker to wall, while the second listens for the echo. He will not hear it so clearly if he stands beside the clicker at point B as he will if he walks to one side and a little behind the clicker to a point such as C. The position where the echo is loudest can be predicted on the same principle that governs the specular reflection of light from mirrors; namely, that the angle of reflection, r (angle EAC), equals the angle of incidence, i (angle DAB). This experiment will give clearer results if the listener stands a little behind the clicker, so that he is shielded from the direct, outgoing click by the horn. The same experiment can be performed more accurately by mounting the clicker on a camera tripod and turning it slowly to different angles relative to the wall. The listener may then move back and forth until he finds the points where he hears the echo most clearly. Or the listener may stand still in various positions while the first person turns the clicker slowly back and forth from right to left according to his instructions. It is remarkable how well the results of such experiments confirm the rule that the angle of reflection equals the angle of incidence.

There is an entirely different situation in which it is easy to experience a simple type of echolocation. When you ride in an automobile, sitting by an open window, you hear a number of sounds from the engine, the tires, and the rush of air past the window. As you drive past a high stone wall, through an underpass, or close to any large surface, these sounds will change in quality. A series of concrete guardrail posts, the masonry posts used to support iron fences, or even a row of wooden fence posts can be detected from a rapid series of swishing sounds as the car moves by. Try listening with your eyes closed as you ride along some familiar route and you may be surprised to find how many places you can recognize by ear. If you find a series of clearly "audible" fence posts, compare their sound effects with those you hear in passing through an underpass. Along the posts it is primarily the high frequencies that return as echoes from the relatively small surfaces; in the underpass almost the whole range of sounds of the car will be reflected from the large wall surface. If you make a careful study of these sounds while your car is driven at about the same speed, you will find that you can learn to recognize many types of structures, such as parked cars, from the echoes which they add to the roughly constant sounds made by your own car.

Echoes are used by bats and men to locate smaller and more elusive objects than the walls of buildings, and some interesting properties of reflected waves become important once we begin to work with smaller objects. After you have acquired some experience with the clicker, it is of interest to try it on trees, telephone poles, or other objects that can easily be found out in the open away from other echo-making objects. With care and practice you can detect trees as small as 6 inches from several feet away, and when this has been accomplished, you can again call upon another person to point the clicker at the tree while you, the listening observer, move about to different positions to find where the echo sounds loudest. The result will usually be that the echo can be heard over a much wider range of angles than happened with the louder echo from a building. This is because the tree is only a little more than one wave length in diameter and the echoes are spread over a much wider range of directions, as indicated in Fig. 10. Just as a horn less than one wave length in size fails to concentrate sound, small objects scatter their echoes. If you can hear echoes from trees or poles as small

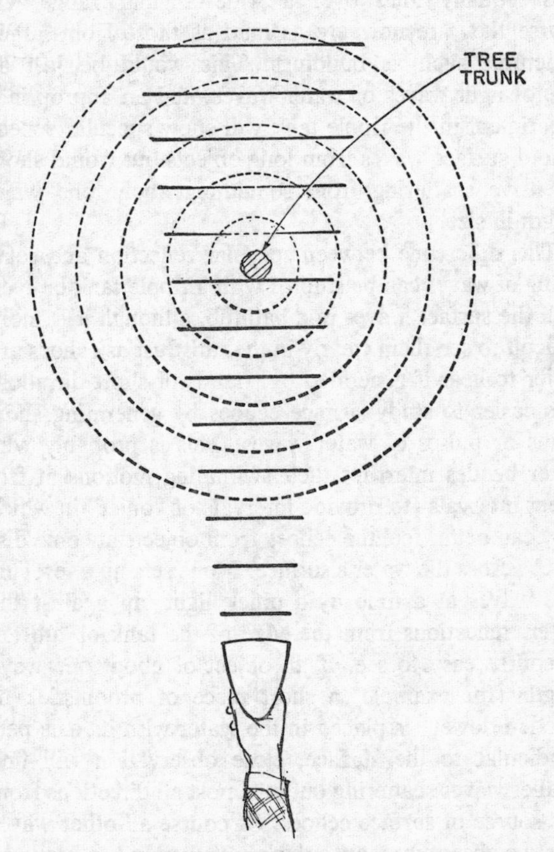

Fig. 10. When the wave length is greater than the size of the object (here a tree trunk), the echo, or scattered sound moves out in all directions. The solid lines indicate the original sound, the dashed lines the echoes, and the width of the lines the intensity of sound.

as one or two wave lengths, you will find them almost equally loud over a wide angular range. Of course they are nowhere as loud as those from larger structures such as buildings. This would be just as true of light waves or water waves, and an appropriate experiment in the ripple tank will show specular reflection of surface waves from long objects but would show extensive scattering from something about one wave length in size.

This difference between specular reflection and scattering of waves can be studied with a ripple tank or even with the surface waves in a bathtub, although it is more difficult to see them clearly in the tub. Just as echoes are easier to hear if generated by sounds of short duration, it is easier to study surface echoes by generating short trains or pulses of water waves. This is probably why water beetles interrupt their swimming motions at frequent intervals—to provide intervals of "quiet" in which they can better feel the echoes from objects at some distance across the water's surface. If one sets up a few surface waves at a time by a quick light tap against the water, reflections from the edge of the tank or tub are of course easy to see. If an object of about one wave length (for example, a short piece of broomstick or wooden dowel) is placed in the water with its axis perpendicular to the surface, close observation will find smaller waves scattering out in almost all directions from this source of surface echoes. Of course all other waves must be absent, but, once this phenomenon has been observed, it is of some interest to vary the size of the cylindrical object from the smallest that produces visible scattered waves up to sizes well in excess of one wave length. Such experiments convince one of the real difference between sharply directional specular reflection and the diffuse scattering from small echo sources. These two general types of echoes will be important when we move on from the physics of echoes to a study of the actual uses to which they are put by blind men and by the bats and other animals which have developed such refined and precise methods of echolocation for the carrying out of their daily business.

CHAPTER 4

The Language of Echoes

From our brief, qualitative look at the remarkable navigational feats of some animals, it seemed clear that sound was a most important message carrier. This led us to a detailed examination of sound itself, particularly how it echoes or reflects, in order that we might experiment more skillfully and intelligently in an attempt to learn how echoes are actually used by animals–what are their limits, what aids or hinders, what physical characteristics are especially suited to echolocation, what are the special characteristics of the sounds these animals make. We may hope to discover some important bits of evidence, perhaps obscure at the moment, which will aid blind people in their travels, and even if this does not occur, we will certainly know our environment better. Men have always learned from animals, and even in this age of electronics and atomic structure we still have much to learn. Since the bats are so expert in the use of echoes, let us begin by examining in more detail the sounds they broadcast to produce the echoes which guide their agile flight.

Orientation Sounds of Bats

Bats make a variety of vocal sounds; for example, when disturbed they squeak and chitter. But we are interested primarily in the sounds they use in flight to generate useful echoes that tell them about objects at some distance. These *orientation sounds* are all of high frequency, though they overlap slightly the range of human hearing to produce the very faint audible ticking we have discussed. But most of the sound energy emitted by flying bats lies at frequencies from 10 to 150 kc in different species, and I will describe only one or two examples of orientation sounds that have been measured from a few typical kinds of bats.

One of the simplest acoustic patterns is that used by the *horseshoe bats,* an insectivorous group that lives in Europe, Asia, Australia, and Africa. They use orientation sounds of nearly a single frequency, which may be anywhere from 60 to 120 kc, depending on the species. The individual sounds last only a small fraction of a second, usually from 50 to 100 milliseconds, but this is much longer than the duration of other bats' sounds. The name horseshoe bat refers to a complicated series of folds or membranes surrounding the nostrils and the mouth with two roughly concentric rosettes which vaguely resemble a horseshoe when viewed from in front. The German zoologist Franz P. Moehres has shown recently that the horseshoe serves as a small horn to concentrate the emitted sound into a narrow beam which is swept back and forth as the bat scans its surroundings. Bats have a habit of hanging head downward by the hind feet, and the horseshoe bats have especially flexible hip joints. They can pivot through almost a complete circle as they scan with their beam of high-frequency sound. Often they dart out from such a position to seize an insect that flies within range.

Another group of bats, confined to the tropics, feed mostly upon fruit, but some also eat insects, which they may pick off the vegetation. These bats emit much fainter sounds than the horseshoe bats—extremely brief clicks, lasting from a fraction of a millisecond to 2 or 3 milliseconds. The sound waves making up these very short pulses are complicated, with a variety of frequencies from as low as 10 to as high as 150 kc, again depending on the species. The vampire bats, which feed on the blood of living animals and men, belong to this group. Without causing the victim to awake from his sleep, they feed by making small cuts with their very sharp teeth and drinking the blood that flows for a time before clotting. None of these bats seems to pursue moving insects from very great distances, and the intensity of their sounds is so low that only the best of microphones and sound-analyzing equipment will register them. They may be called *whispering bats* to distinguish them from the other two groups.

The third major category includes the common insectivorous bats that are well known in North America and Europe. With a very few exceptions, these bats all hunt flying insects in the open, tracking their elusive moving prey on the wing, maneuvering through complicated split-second turns and other acrobatics to follow and intercept the erratic flight of moths and flying beetles, May flies and mosquitoes. The sounds used by this group, only a few milliseconds in duration and almost as intense as those of the horseshoe bats, have a characteristic frequency pattern. Each orientation sound starts at a very high frequency and drops rapidly during its brief life, to end about an octave below the frequency at which it started. The common little brown bats of the

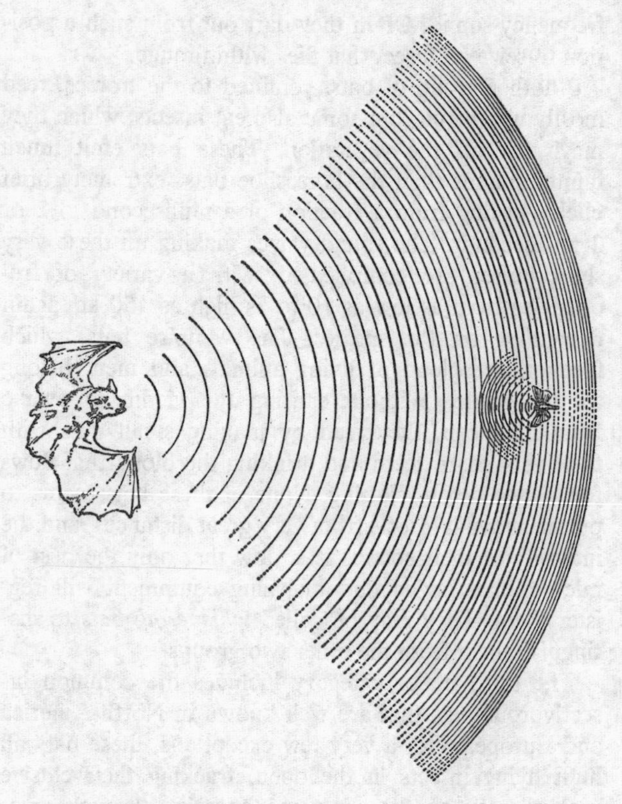

Fig. 11. The frequency and wave length of a bat's sound vary during each chirp. This diagram, which is approximately to scale, illustrates the small amount of sound reflected by one insect.

United States begin each of their orientation sounds at about 90 kc and end at 45 kc. Since each sound lasts only about 2 milliseconds, this is a very rapid change in frequency; indeed, this bat sweeps through a frequency band double the whole range of the human ear in 2 milliseconds. As illustrated in Fig. 11, a typical orientation sound contains only about 50 sound waves, no two exactly alike. The wave length of the initial waves is only half the wave length of those making up the end of the emitted sound. These sounds are *chirps,* at least that is what we call audible sounds made by certain insects when they sweep through as wide a range of frequencies within a fraction of a second. This type is sometimes called a frequency-modulated pulse of sound, and this group of bats may be thought of as "FM bats" in contrast to the horseshoe bats with their much longer, sharply beamed tones of nearly constant frequency, and the faint but complex clicks of the tropical "whispering bats."

Echoes of Insect Prey

The FM or chirping bats have been studied much more thoroughly than the other two groups; therefore, more is known about them. They seem to be the most highly specialized for a life of flight, very expert at maneuvering under the most difficult conditions. The daily (or nightly) business of catching insect food compels them to be highly skilled in the detection of such small moving objects and in the aerial acrobatics necessary to intercept them. Since bats do almost all their hunting on dark nights, often approaching insects from above or in wooded areas where they would have to be seen against a dark background, visual detection must be impossible. And Spallanzani, as we have said in Chapter 1, showed before 1800 that blind bats catch as many insects as normal animals. It has usually been thought that they located insects by listening for the sounds of their wingbeats, and this probably does occur in some circumstances when the flying insects make appreciable humming or buzzing noises. Locating insects by such passive listening would seem to call for silence on the bat's part, but the chirps are emitted at higher and higher rates as the bats locate and close in upon flying insects. Furthermore, bats will often pursue imitation insects such as pebbles or little wads of wet absorbent cotton tossed gently into the air as they fly by. They do not actually bite or swallow such decoys, but they swoop avidly towards them with the same increase in the tempo of the orientation sounds they employ when chasing real insects under natural conditions. When one realizes how silent are many of the small insects upon which bats feed, it becomes rather likely, though not rigorously proven, that the bats detect at least some of their insect prey by hearing echoes of their own chirps bouncing off the insects rather than relying solely on the sounds emitted by the insects themselves.

I shall return a little later to the patterns in which these orientation sounds are broadcast under various conditions, including the pursuit of insect prey. But first let us consider the effectiveness of the process of insect hunting. Just how many insects does a bat catch in a given time? How big are the insects caught? At what distances are they detected? Only very recently have we been able to provide even partial and tentative answers to such questions. Spallanzani and others who examined the stomachs of bats just returned from a night's hunting have marveled at the relatively large mass of finely chewed insect remains present in the digestive tract of every successful bat. One study showed that little brown bats weighing 7 grams commonly catch 1 gram of insects per hour of active hunting. Very recently we have been able to persuade a few bats to hunt insects in a laboratory flight room where the process could be studied and photographed. One smaller relative of the little brown bat, weighing only 3.5 grams, caught mosquitoes at such a rapid rate before our very eyes that after 15 minutes' hunting its weight had increased by 10 per cent to 3.85 grams. These particular mosquitoes weighed about 0.002 gram each. The bat had no possible way of gaining weight during these 15 minutes of closely observed hunting, aside from the weight of the mosquitoes caught. It drank no water and ate nothing else. It probably *lost* a little weight by the evaporation of water while breathing; therefore, it caught more than 0.35 gram of mosquitoes.

Dividing the weight gain by the weight of a single mosquito shows that at least 175 mosquitoes were caught in 15 minutes, or more than one every 6 seconds. This was also approximately the number of obvious mosquito-chasing maneuvers that we could count during this hunting spree. There is every reason to believe that similar rates of insect capture are commonplace events in the nightly activities of millions of these bats and their relatives all over the world. Of course, it is not always mosquitoes that are eaten; almost any kind of insect that is locally available and is not too big seems welcome. Sometimes moths up to an inch in wingspread are taken, but at other times these bats capture insects much smaller than mosquitoes. In one instance a small gnat weighing only 0.0002 gram was found still unswallowed in the mouth of a bat killed while it was hunting.

This maneuvering to capture one insect every 6 seconds is what makes the flight of bats appear so erratic. Far from being feeble fliers buffeted about by air currents, they are expert fliers engaging in the difficult interception of flying insects. Their percentage of successes must be very high indeed. Certainly they are doing vastly better than simply flying around with their mouths open. Even when mosquitoes are particularly abundant, their density is such that one of these small bats would have to fly all night before its mouth encountered a single mosquito purely by chance. Yet the actual rate of capture is one every few seconds.

Analysis of many cases has shown that when a little brown bat is flying fairly straight and is not close to anything of immediate concern, it repeats its 1- and 2-millisecond chirps at rates of 10 to 20 per second. But whenever it approaches any small obstacles, such as wires stretched across a laboratory room to test its skill, many more chirps are emitted in a given interval of time. For brief periods the repetition rate may rise as high as 250 per second. When this happens, the individual chirps become shorter, usually less than 1 millisecond, so that silent intervals still exist between chirps. When the high-frequency sounds of these bats are studied under natural conditions, a clear distinction between straight and level flight and the active pursuit of flying insects becomes apparent. Such eavesdropping is only possible, of course, when we have apparatus which will detect the bat sounds conveniently. One device rectifies the bat pulse and thus "translates" each of the bat's high-frequency sounds into audible clicks in earphones or a small loudspeaker. This makes it possible to watch the bat while at the same time "listening" to its orientation sounds in this transposed form.

When this "listening" apparatus is used in some spot where bats do their insect hunting, we notice that one cruising past on a straight course several feet above the ground sounds like the slow putt-putt-putt-putt of a lazy, old gasoline engine. Often it will fly straight past with little or no change in this rhythm, but if its attention is attracted either to a real insect or to a decoy, such as a pebble tossed up in front of it, then there is a marked increase in the rate of the orientation sounds. Sometimes this is a slight increase in rate, but if the pursuit is serious, involving drastic maneuvers such as sudden turns, wingovers, or sharp dives, then the translation resembles the acceleration of a motorcycle engine. On occasion it rises to a real crescendo with the individual clicks coming so close together that for human ears they fuse into a whining buzz reminiscent of a chain saw.

Recent experiments in collaboration with F. A. Webster have provided conclusive evidence that little brown bats can intercept fruit flies entirely by echolocation. Especially cooperative bats became accustomed to catching fruit flies in a small room where their rate of catching could be measured, as with the mosquitoes, by weighing the bat before and after a few minutes of active hunting. Their maneuvers were photographed on sound film, along with the position of the fly, and the translated orientation sounds were registered on the sound track. The repetition rate of the orientation chirps increased on the average at half a meter from the fruit fly. Total darkness together with very loud hissing noise covering the whole range of human hearing had no effect at all on the rate of insect catching. But in a rather mild and unevenly distributed ultrasonic noise the bats gave up all attempts to hunt. Complete catching maneuvers required less than half a second, and in several cases a successful catch was followed in less than one second by another buzz and the capture of a second fruit fly.

Precision of Echolocation

Another important aspect of bats' use of echoes for rapid and precise navigation is the small size of objects which can be detected and the distances at which detection can occur. The only feasible tests yet devised have involved wires or strings rather than small isolated ob-

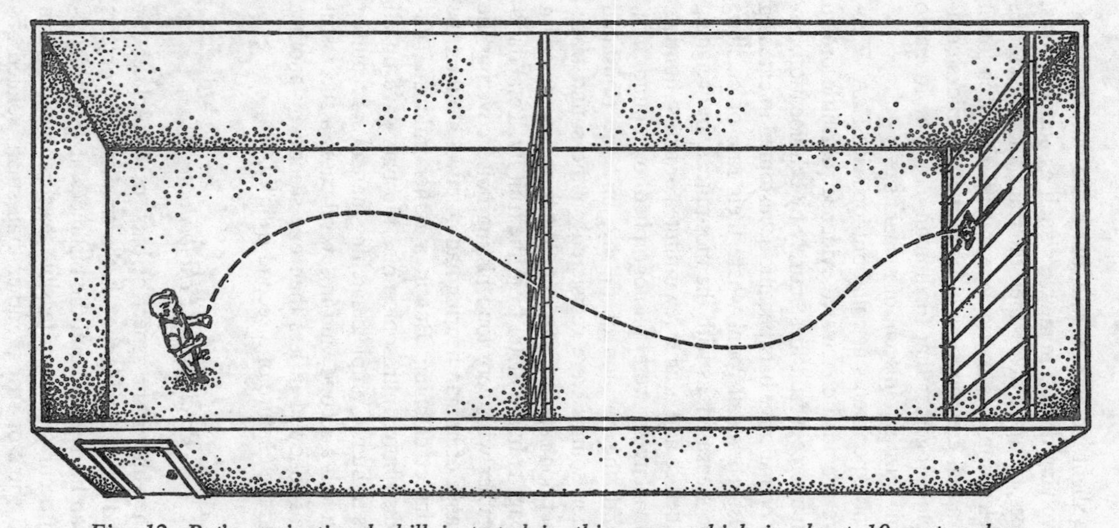

Fig. 12. Bat's navigational skill is tested in this room which is about 10 meters long and 3 meters wide. One row of wires is in the middle of the room and the second row is about 45 centimeters from the end wall.

jects like insects or pebbles. It is simply too difficult to keep small particles stationary in the air long enough to make accurate tests of bats' ability to dodge them. When wires are strung across a laboratory "flight" room, on the other hand, as diagramed in Fig. 12, the animals seem anxious to avoid collisions, although the brown bats weigh so little that they do not seem to be injured even in an occasional head-on crash against a taut wire.

When the wires are spaced 30 centimeters apart, or slightly more than the wingspread of the little brown bat, they make a difficult barrier that even the most skillful animals brush against lightly from time to time. The wires can be made smaller and smaller, without any marked effect on the percentage of misses registered by a really skillful animal, down to a wire diameter of a fraction of a millimeter. To be sure, many bats will be found on first testing in such an obstacle course to be clumsy, striking even the larger wires, but this is usually because they are in poor condition or not completely awakened from the deep sleep into which they lapse even on summer days. It is necessary to reduce the wire diameter to 0.07 millimeter (about the diameter of a human hair) before the little brown bats strike them at random. Even slightly larger wires, 0.12 millimeters in diameter, while difficult to miss, are dodged by the really skillful "athletes" among our experimental subjects far more often than one would expect.

Astonishing as it is that bats can detect wires as small as 0.12 millimeter, this type of experiment does not tell us at what distance this detection occurs. But motion pictures of the bats will give some indication of the range of detection when the translated orientation sounds are put on a sound track of the movie. Careful study of such movies, frame by frame, has enabled us to find the distance at which the rate of repetition of the bats' chirps first begins to increase. This varies from flight to flight, even for a single individual, but the average of numerous measurements with several sizes of wire gave the following results.

Diameter of wires (millimeters)	Average rep. rate before approach to wires (pulses/sec)	Average maximum rep. rate (pulses/sec)	Average distance at which rep. rate first increases (centimeters)
3.0	12	50	215
1.07	12	40	185
0.65	13	30	150
0.46	13	40	120
0.28	12	27	105
0.18	12	22	90

These distances are considerably greater than one would guess from the bat's flight behavior. Ordinarily it flies along a fairly straight course and swerves only in the last few inches to avoid a wire. Yet the increasing pulse rate shows that it has already detected the wires and reacted to them at the distances shown in the table. If no wire is in place, there is no increase in the rate of the orientation chirps. Of course, a bat might be aware of the wires at still greater distances than the table shows, but it gives no sign of such awareness that we yet have learned to recognize. The important point is that even such small wires as those 0.18 millimeters in diameter are detected at some distance, not merely at the last possible moment to avoid collision. It is also interesting to note that small wires produce only a small increase in pulse rate. Actually the bat is moving so fast (approximately 4 meters per second) that with the smaller wires it often has time for only 2 or 3 additional pulses above the number it would have employed had there been no wire in place. All these facts testify that the echolocation practiced by bats is a refined, accurate method of orientation, not merely a crude sort of groping.

Bread upon the Waters

Nor do these examples by any means exhaust the list of difficult tasks which bats accomplish with some aid at least from echolocation. Certain of the whispering bats catch insects, small birds, or lizards that are resting on vegetation, but we are not sure that they do this by means of echolocation. They may simply listen to characteristic sounds coming from their prey. More amazing is the fact that four different species of the FM bats make their living by catching fish. This they do by flying just above the surface of the water and every now and then dipping their hind feet just below the surface. The claws on these feet are long, curved, and sharp, and the bats manage to gaff small minnows often enough to fill their stomachs every evening (as shown in Fig. 13). When fishing in this way on the darkest nights (and often with mist rising from the water), they emit a rapid series of chirps much like those of their insect-catching relatives. The gap between the two types of food gathering is not as great as it might at first seem, for the insectivorous bats drink by skimming the surface of the water and dipping their chins just deep enough to secure a drop of water at a time. This requires fine control, for a millimeter too deep would surely result in a dunking. These insectivorous bats also catch insects resting on the water surface, so perhaps it was a small step from this habit to reach for fish swimming just at the surface. These fish-catching species make much of their living in this way, and during their recent evolutionary history a relatively small anatomical adaptation has resulted in the specialized fish-gaffing claws.

When I have watched these bats in Panama, I have seen no sign that the fish were moving or disturbing the surface of the water in any way. Often it was glassy calm, and the bat flew for hundreds of feet a few inches above the surface, quickly lowering the hind feet into the water for a short distance and then raising them while continuing its low-altitude searching flight. How do these bats know where fish are to be captured? They are evi-

Fig. 13. Motion pictures of fishing bats actually gaffing minnows provided the model for this drawing. Prentice Bloedel took the photographs.

dently selective in their fishing, for they fly long distances just above the water and only rarely dip their claws beneath the surface. Since the fishing occurs on dark and misty nights, it is most unlikely that the fish could be seen and still less probable that they emit any sound audible to the bat flying in the air above the surface. Could it be that the fish-catching bats detect echoes from fish beneath the surface? At first glance this may seem only a slight modification of the process by which closely related bats catch insects in the air. But the physical discontinuity between air and water makes the transmission of sound difficult, and so echolocation seems an unlikely explanation.

As mentioned earlier in connection with the underwater hearing of fish and porpoises, sound waves have great difficulty in passing from air to water or vice versa. When airborne sound impinges on a smooth surface of water, with its direction of travel perpendicular to the water surface, only 0.12 per cent of the energy of the airborne sound continues beneath the surface as underwater sound waves. For a sound wave traveling from water to air, the same small fraction of the acoustic energy striking the surface from below continues outwards into the air. This means that a flying bat's orientation sounds striking the water, penetrating into it, being reflected back from a fish, and passing out into the air again would be reduced to $(0.0012)^2$, or 1.44×10^{-6} of the original sound, during the two trips through the air-water interface. To this great reduction must be added further losses: only a small fraction of the emitted sound would be reflected by a fish, and only a small fraction of what did escape into the air would strike the ears of the listening bat.

Let us grant all these difficulties that a hypothesis of echolocation of fish through the water surface would face. How then do these bats manage to catch their fish? To study this fish-catching behavior in greater detail we built an outdoor flight cage in Trinidad, at the William Beebe Tropical Research Station of the New York Zoological Society. In this 4- by 15-meter cage there is a 2- by 7-meter pool where Roderick Suthers and I have been able to observe the fish-catching of the bulldog bat, the best known of the species that feed on fish as well as insects. Its name derives from its large overhanging lips. In this outdoor laboratory we could vary the conditions to learn what factors are of greatest importance in the detection and seizing of food at or below the water surface. Since minnows usually swam too deep for the bats to reach, we experimented for the most part with chunks of fish about half an inch in size. We attached them to fine vertical wires tied to an underwater holder that could be moved to vary the position of the food morsel both vertically and horizontally.

To induce the bulldog bats to take pieces of fish in this somewhat unnatural situation, the wires were first adjusted to hold the chunks a few millimeters above the surface. Hungry bats were quick to snatch these morsels, and their orientation sounds speeded up in repetition rate just as they do in insect hunting. Blindfolded bats were just as quick and accurate in seizing fish from the wires; vision was evidently not necessary for this type of fishing. When the wires were lowered into the water gradually the bats continued to locate and gaff the fish chunks whenever they broke the surface. But when the fish was totally submerged the bats found it only by chance as they dipped their feet and dragged their gaff-like claws more or less at random across the pool. If the fish do provide detectable echoes of bats' orientation sounds, it might well be the air in their swim bladders that scatters the sound rather than the actual body tissues of the fish, which are acoustically very similar to water. But our captive bats never displayed any ability to seek out and locate wholly submerged pieces of fish more often than expected by chance, whether or not they contained air-filled bladders.

Fish may be detected in nature only when they disturb the water surface or jump into the air. Suthers' experiments showed bulldog bats to be very sensitive to echoes from small objects protruding above the water surface. They even learned which of many such objects marked the location of food. In some experiments he mounted the chunk of fish 1 or 2 millimeters below the surface, where by itself it could not be detected, but added a fine vertical wire close beside the submerged fish extending a few millimeters up through the surface into the air. Several bats learned to recognize the wires as markers for submerged fish, and their outstretched claws usually reached down accurately enough to carry off the piece of fish.

Sometimes the bulldog bats fish over waters that are rippled by the wind, and it is not yet clear how they distinguish the shifting echoes of ripples from those caused by a small fish at or just below the surface. This problem is typical of many unanswered questions about these fishing bats as well as other bats that live in tropical regions; many more investigations will be needed to explain the full role of echolocation in their diversified ways of life.

Resistance to Jamming

Up to this point we have been thinking about echoes as more or less isolated sound waves that could be dealt with one at a time. To be sure, we considered earlier the likelihood that a faint echo would be masked by the louder outgoing sound. Experiments described in Chapter 3 demonstrated that human hearing ignores echoes arriving within a small fraction of a second after a loud sharp click. Bats obviously do better than we in discriminating these echoes from the original sound. In the experiments of Schevill and Lawrence a porpoise showed that it could detect echoes from a small fish despite the louder competing echoes from the bottom of the pond, the surface, and the shore a few feet beyond this small-sized target. But the expertness of bats goes even further than anything we have yet considered. When they are hunting insects, their ears receive a more complicated mixture of sounds than merely their original chirp plus a single echo returning from a single insect and having the same wave form at a lower energy level. What really impinges upon their ears is a whole series of echoes from everything within several feet—the ground, other insects, and every bush, twig, tree trunk, leaf, or blade of grass. Many of these things contribute only small amounts of echo energy, but the echo from an insect is itself a faint one, and if it is audible so must the others be. How then do bats sort out one class of faint echoes from all the others? How do they hear the difference between echoes that mean food to be caught and those that mean obstacles to be dodged?

If we knew how bats discriminate so expertly between faint insect echoes and the competing echoes arriving within a small fraction of a second, we could make more rapid progress toward solving the orientation problems of blind people, to say nothing of developing instruments that could emulate the bats more perfectly. Unfortunately this is not yet possible, but it is interesting to consider how well bats can make such discriminations. This cannot be easy, even for a bat, and faint echoes from wire obstacles are less skillfully utilized when stronger echoes arrive in the same small fraction of a second. For example, we once performed an experiment in which two rows of wires were stretched across a flight room, one row at the middle of the room and the other row 45 centimeters from the end wall, as diagramed in Fig. 12. In both rows the wires extended from floor to ceiling and were spaced 30 centimeters apart. When the diameter of the wires was 0.46 millimeter, they were difficult echo targets, but the percentage of misses in a large number of flights through the central row was 91 per cent. This represents a considerable degree of success, and almost all the contacts were very light touches when the bat did not quite manage to time its wingbeats so that the wing tips cleared the obstacle.

When the same animals not only flew through the middle row but also continued on through the end row, their success was much less—the percentage of misses fell from 91 per cent at the middle row to 58 per cent for the end row which was 45 centimeters from the end wall. This result was probably due to the very much larger echo from the end wall. The situation can be understood in terms of Fig. 14, a schematic graph of the sound energy reaching the bat's ears during the fraction of a second when each chirp is emitted and its several echoes return. The upper graph (A) depicts the situation when the middle row of wires is being detected and avoided; the middle graph (B) applies to the same size of wire located 45 centimeters from the end wall, while the third graph (C) describes a further experiment in which the wires near the end wall were 1.07 millimeters in diameter. In C, the bat's success was about the same (88 per cent misses) as it had been with the 0.46 millimeter wires at the middle of the flight room (A). Under natural conditions the important echoes would be those from an insect rather than a wire, and the competing echoes would arrive from many different objects, such as the ground, tree trunks, or branches of trees. These would produce more complicated echoes than those from the end wall of the flight room and would be present over a longer period of time, but they would never include as strong a single echo as that from the large end wall. An approximation to this case is represented in the fourth graph (D) of Fig. 14, where it has been assumed that some of the extraneous echoes have come from objects closer than the insect itself. This must happen when bats hunt, as they often do,

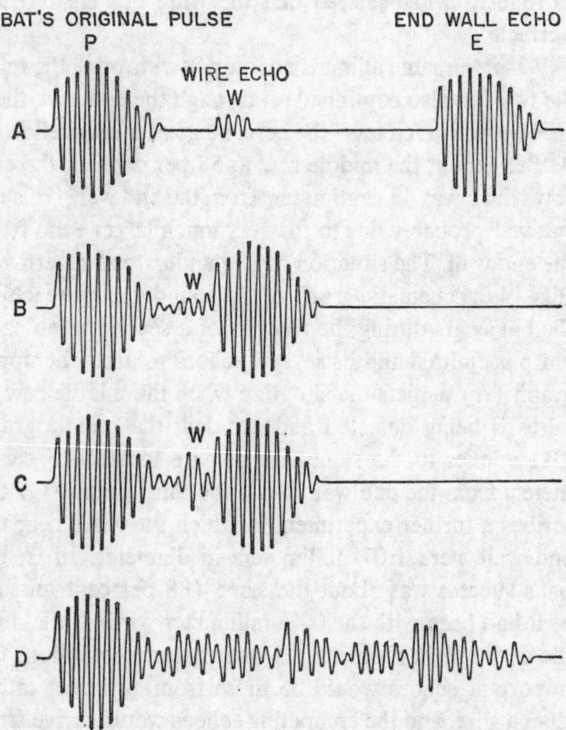

Fig. 14. Schematic graphs of a bat's chirp and the echoes in the flight room (Fig. 12) under various test conditions: A—approaching 0.46-millimeter wires in the middle of room; B—approaching same wires near the end wall; C—approaching larger wires close to the end wall (note the larger echo); and D—approaching an insect under natural conditions in woods where many other objects also return echoes. (For simplicity the frequency modulation is not shown.)

in thickly wooded areas where competing echoes obscure the important echo from the insect.

The success of bats in catching one insect every few seconds testifies to their ability not only to hear the insect echoes but to sort them out of a welter of other, competing echoes. This process has been studied in the laboratory by modifying the circumstances to standardize the conditions and permit measurements of the bats' performance. Rather than studying bats as they hunt insects in the woods, we generated artificial sounds in our flight room so that these noises were added to the echoes from wires, floor, and walls. In other words, we tried to confuse or "jam" the bats. The result was a surprising and revealing failure. The bats continued to dodge fine wires even in noise equal in total intensity to their emitted sounds. The bats clearly preferred not to fly in noise, but if forced to do so they could detect wires even when the noise blanketed a good part, but not all, of their octave or more of frequency sweep. They dodged wires better in intermittent noise (on and off every millisecond) than in the same noise uninterrupted. They can thus exploit any gaps in time or frequency coverage of a jamming noise; this ability may explain how they avoid mutual interference when several fly close to each other. Only rarely will one bat's echoes coincide exactly in both time and frequency with the emitted sounds of another.

In experiments with a species of bat that emits rather faint orientation sounds, a sufficient number of jamming loudspeakers generating very loud, broad band noise did prevent them from dodging 1-millimeter wires. But these bats could take advantage of differences in the direction from which noise and echoes reached their ears to detect echoes having less energy than the jamming noise at all the frequencies involved.

(*Listening in the Dark* has a more detailed account of these experiments.)

What emerges from these several examples of orientation based on echoes is the simple fact that bats and porpoises are most adept at locating small and distant objects in this way. Furthermore, they do so with a precision and acuity that are understandable only when one remembers that this is how they make their living. If a bat fumbles with its echoes, it goes hungry. Hunger is a powerful incentive, tending strongly to improve any mechanism or process subjected to this selective action. This is what biologists call *natural selection,* the process responsible for the evolution of plants and animals into their many diversified and complex forms. It is a slow process but an extremely effective one, and in the bats and porpoises we see the end result achieved through natural selection, perfecting over millions of years the animals' faculties for utilizing echoes. Finally, it is important to realize that the use of echoes requires the bats and porpoises to possess more than merely a means for generating sounds that in turn will yield echoes. It is also essential that these animals discriminate certain important echoes from complex mixtures of other sounds that are often much louder than those conveying the crucial information about food.

Discrimination of one portion of a complex sound from louder components is not a special skill of bats and porpoises. All animals endowed with a sense of hearing discriminate, and in many respects the human ear and brain are the best of all. When we listen to speech or music, we sort out a few significant portions of a complicated mixture of shifting wave forms. If we hear people speaking an unknown foreign language, we receive a similar jumble of sound waves, but one to which we have no key. Footsteps or bat chirps and their echoes are a special language of their own. It is much simpler than German, Chinese, or English, but men, particularly blind men, find it very difficult to learn this language. Yet bats no larger than a baby mouse understand it well enough to catch ten mosquitoes every minute in the dark. What is it in a bat's tiny brain that permits understanding of this language and unlocks this library of useful information? No one yet knows the answer. We cannot even be sure we are asking the proper questions.

Bats have been hunting moths and other insects by echolocation for millions of years, and certain of the moths have developed protective mechanisms in the course of their evolution. These have been analyzed through a series of brilliant experiments carried out by K. D. Roeder and A. Treat. The moths often change their flight patterns abruptly at the onset of high frequency sounds. They can do this because they have relatively large and specialized tympanic organs which serve as ears, although they are located in chambers at the sides of the thorax and not in the head. Each tympanic organ contains a very thin membrane similar to our eardrum, but only two sensory cells and nerve fibers are stimulated by the motion of each membrane in response to sound waves. With so few auditory nerve cells the moth cannot discriminate between different frequencies, but its ears are sensitive to a wide range of frequencies from well within the range of human hearing up to the ultrasonic frequencies used by bats.

While moth ears are stimulated by almost any high frequency sound, the behavioral responses are highly variable. The moth may do nothing, and in that case it is quite likely to be captured by an attacking bat. Or it may shift its flight to erratic loops or dive to the ground. Moths that execute these evasive maneuvers are much more likely to escape. Why then do some moths fail to respond? One explanation is that this variability may discourage the bats from adopting better interception tactics; thus, while some moths are more easily captured the species as a whole is better served. This whole subject of offensive and defensive adaptations of bats and moths is well described in Roeder's book *Nerve Cells and Insect Behavior*.

Quite recent investigations have disclosed that some moths emit sharp bat-like clicks. Perhaps these clicks serve to confuse an attacking bat, although they are not intense enough to cause serious jamming. This question is still being studied, and the evidence is not yet conclusive. For the present we cannot be certain whether or not active acoustic countermeasures are employed by some species of moths. But when one pauses to reflect that thirty years ago the very existence of echolocation in bats was merely an unsupported conjecture, it is clearly best to keep an open mind for more surprises in the future.

CHAPTER 5

Sonar and Radar

Although men have not learned the "language of echoes," they have been remarkably successful in designing echolocating instruments which surpass those of animals in many ways but remain quite inferior in other respects. What are these instruments and how do they compare with analogous living mechanisms in the bodies of bats, porpoises, or whirligig beetles? Footsteps and clickers are simple devices that help blind people create more useful echoes, but the receiving instrument is still the human ear. Perhaps blind men will some day learn to exploit the potentialities of the matchless human brain for a better comprehension of the language of echoes. But, in the meantime, it is important to appreciate the devices which men have contrived to carry out both the sending and the receiving functions of echolocation. These mechanisms have been developed for very practical, often military, purposes, excelling particularly in the great distances over which they operate. If they utilize sound waves, they are usually called *sonar* systems. If electromagnetic waves are employed, they are called *radar* systems. Sonar is used by man almost exclusively for underwater echolocation, while radar is used only in air or outer space.

Echoes under Water

The tragic sinking of the *Titanic* by an iceberg in 1912 prompted the first of many efforts to invent a means of detecting icebergs in darkness or in fog. Even in 1959, icebergs caused the sinking of an ocean liner fully equipped with modern aids to navigation. Sir Hiram Maxim, a prolific inventor who in the late nineteenth century attempted to build flying machines, proposed that bats' methods of navigation be copied directly in the design of safety devices for ocean-going ships. Unfortunately, however, he did not really know how bats navigate—for the simple reason that the subject had been largely neglected since the days of Spallanzani. He surmised correctly that bats used echolocation but was incorrect when he assumed that the probing sound came from the beating of their wings. Hence he advised that ships generate very *low*-frequency sounds of roughly 15 c.p.s. and that receiving devices for such frequencies be mounted on the bow of the ship. Faint echoes from this sound were to ring a small bell, loud ones a large gong, so that the crew could judge the seriousness of the danger.

Maxim's idea was, nevertheless, a step forward in understanding bat navigation, for it introduced for the first time the idea that sounds inaudible to human ears might be the basis of bats' uncanny ability to fly in darkness. But his ideas did not lead to any practical method for detecting icebergs, and for at least two important reasons. In the first place, the low frequencies which he proposed meant that long wave lengths would have been involved; 15-c.p.s. sound has a 20-meter wave. It s now well known that objects whose size is much less han the wave length of the sound being used yield only aint echoes, but in 1912 this was not a generally appreiated fact. Had scientists been less scornful of bats and ad they known more about "Spallanzani's bat probem," more progress would have been made by 1912. Furthermore, Maxim proposed to echolocate icebergs hrough the air, whereas both the actual danger to the hip and the major part of the iceberg lay beneath the urface. The latter consideration led other inventors to nvestigate the possibility of using underwater sound.

Two or three years after the sinking of the *Titanic,* he increasing use of submarines by the German Navy purred the development of underwater sound devices. At first it was largely a matter of listening to the sounds originating from the submarine, particularly from its engines and propellers. Much of the naval use of underwater sound is still passive listening for the sounds of other ships. But to a small degree by 1918, and to a much greater extent by 1940, research had led to active probing of the sea with sounds which would yield usable echoes. Enemy submarines were the main military targets, but along with the development of sonar came the echo sounder, or fathometer, a device to measure the depth of the water. In comparison with an enemy submarine (or the fish detected by porpoises), the bottom of the ocean would seem to be an easy target, but for many years the idea proved simpler than its realization. In the deeper parts of the ocean even an echo from the bottom was faint and difficult to detect with the early sonar devices, but the most critical problem came when the water was shallower and more dangerous. Here the difficulty was that the ship's hull had a disconcerting tendency to "ring" or prolong the outgoing sound even after the actual generating mechanism had been turned off. The combined sound lasted much longer than th time required for it to make the round trip to the bot tom. In other words, there were severe problems of *dis crimination*—separating relatively faint echoes from th continuing, original emitted sound. The instrument were confronted with the same problems as those tha make a blind man less skilled at echolocation than porpoise or a bat. This engineering problem was solve in part by learning how to make underwater sounds o shorter duration.

By the 1950s, however, echo sounders had been per fected to a level of reliability where they have become al most essential for safe navigation. They even became s sensitive that they began to indicate "false bottoms" be tween the ship and the true bottom. "Finding" two o three extra ocean bottoms above the real one was rather disconcerting discovery, but after a time the fish ermen who used echo sounders began to notice that som of the "false bottoms" were really echoes from school of fish. Still later, mysterious layers of faint echoing, o sound scattering, were noted almost everywhere in dee oceans at several hundred feet below the surface. Thes have been called the *deep scattering layers* and they wer later found to migrate up and down with dawn and dusk This fact provided the clue to their identity.

Oceanographers had already discovered by systemati netting operations that large populations of shrimp an other small marine animals live at depths where sunligh barely penetrates. This depth is greater at noon than a midnight; hence there is a massive vertical migration o these animals upward during the evening and dow again at daybreak. The physical records of the dee scattering layers turned out to match the known be havior of the animals. Once this additional fact was es tablished, the echo sounder became a valuable tool fo biological research, for now the timing of the vertical migrations could be studied with great precision. Of course the echoes from a deep scattering layer do not identify the actual animals, so we still do not know for certain whether the principal sources of these echoes are shrimp-like animals, fish, or possibly squid.

Sonar systems effective at echolocating submarines were used with great success in World War II. One of these sonar systems has a transmitting hydrophone, or underwater loudspeaker which broadcasts sound whose power level is 600 watts. For comparison, the minimum sound power level audible in a quiet room at the frequencies to which the human ear is most sensitive is 10^{-16} watt, while a very loud shout at close range has a power of 10^{-4} watt. Thus this sonar system puts into the ocean a sound power roughly equivalent to that of 6,000,000 loud shouts. These intense probing sounds are emitted as short pulses lasting one or two tenths of a second. The frequency can be set anywhere between 10,000 and 26,000 c.p.s. Since the velocity of sound in sea water is about 1500 meters/second, the actual wave lengths of these sounds are from 5 to 13 centimeters, and the length of the pulse is from 150 to 300 meters.

Because this system emits some frequencies above the range of human hearing, there has to be a system to make these frequencies audible. You may be familiar with the "beat note," or "beat frequency" which is conspicuous when two nearly identical notes are sounded simultaneously. If one note is 500 c.p.s. and the other is 600 c.p.s., you will hear a third note of 100 c.p.s. Hence in the electrical circuit of the sonar apparatus, by generating a local frequency and combining with it the incoming echo, an audible beat note is generated. For instance, an incoming echo of 22,000 c.p.s. and a local frequency of 23,000 c.p.s. produce an audible note of 1000 c.p.s. Since the emitted sounds were of short duration, the beat note was also short and sounded like "ping." So familiar was this noise to antisubmarine sailors that probing with sound came to be called "pinging."

In selecting the frequencies of the underwater sound which will produce the most useful echoes, the same general considerations apply as apply to echolocation by bats or blind men. Short pulses are desirable because they allow the emitted sound to end before the echo returns. This means that the frequency of the waves within the pulse cannot be too low; otherwise the pulse duration allows time for only one or two sound waves. Even submarines are small enough targets that long wave lengths could become inefficient owing to the smaller echo returned by an object smaller than one wave length. Furthermore, the background noise always present in the sea is greater at lower frequencies. On the other hand, in water as in air, there is an increasing loss of sound energy as the frequency increases because of the absorption of sound as it travels through the water. Bats have evolved a most satisfactory machinery for echolocation, but men designing sonar systems had to balance all these factors against one another in reaching the compromise choice of 10,000–26,000 c.p.s. as a useful range for practical echo ranging.

In view of the fact that many of the most successful bats use signals with a rapid frequency change during each brief pulse of sound, it is interesting to find that sonar engineers developed a somewhat similar procedure which sometimes improves the performance of the system. In one type of operation the frequency of the emitted sonar signal was varied continuously from 800 c.p.s. above to 800 cycles below the regular frequency. This change was made to occur, as it does in the pulses of the FM bats, during each individual pulse of sound. When the echoes of such pulses were received, the frequency change was audible in the beat note. In one typical setting of the apparatus the transmitted frequency, and of course the echo, was varied from 20,800 to 19,200 c.p.s. If the local frequency was set at 19,000 c.p.s., the beat note would vary from 1800 to 200 c.p.s. and this would produce an extreme chirp or "Wheeoough" sound. One advantage of this type of operation was that at any particular instant of time the many reverberations or multiple echoes from the ship's hull and the water surface had traveled different distances and hence had different frequencies as they arrived at the receiving hydrophone. This tended to create an audible difference between the important chirping echoes from a submarine and the noise level of reverberation from which they had to be discriminated. The important echo was a clear chirp, the competing reverberations an irregular and shifting mixture of frequencies. Very likely bats obtain a similar advantage from their frequency-modulated pulses.

In another type of operation the sonar system used a constant frequency in the emitted pulse, and the operator listened for slight differences in the pitch of the audible beat note. Slight differences between the echo frequency and the local frequency can produce large changes in the audible ping. These differences can be used to determine the relative motion of the target by means of what is called the *Doppler effect*. This change in frequency resulting from the motion of the source causes the rising pitch of a train whistle as the train approaches you. To understand the Doppler effect, let us consider a concrete example. Suppose that the sonar ship is moving east at 10 meters per second while emitting a 0.1 second pulse of 20,000 c.p.s. sound, that is,

2000 sound waves altogether. Let us simplify our arithmetic by assuming that the velocity of sound in sea water is exactly 1500 meters per second. If the ship were stationary, the pulse would occupy 1500 × 0.1, or 150 meters of distance through the water. But it is moving at 10 meters per second, or 1 meter in the one tenth second required to emit the 2000-wave pulse. Since the transmitting hydrophone pursued the sound waves and covered 1 meter while emitting the pulse, the train of waves was thereby compressed into 149 meters instead of 150. This does not affect the velocity of sound in sea water, so that a passing porpoise would hear the pulse as 2000 waves occupying 149 meters and traveling like all other sound waves at 1500 meters per second. All the waves of the pulse strike the porpoise in 140/1500, or 0.099 second, and their frequency would therefore be 2000 waves in 0.099 second, or 20,202 c.p.s. In other words, the emitted pulse has a higher frequency to the listening porpoise because the ship has moved during the process of emitting it. The velocity of sound depends entirely upon the medium in which it is traveling, not upon the velocity of the sound source.

Let us carry our example a little further and suppose that this pulse strikes a submarine which is moving west, toward the sonar ship, also at 10 meters per second. The pulse, which was 149 meters long as it passed the porpoise, is further compressed during the 0.1 second while it is colliding with the oncoming submarine. As it is bouncing back from the target, it is again compressed, both times by the same factor of 149/150. It is not necessarily easy to see why this compression occurs *twice* on striking the submarine, but an imaginary modification of the physical events may help. Suppose that the submarine did not return the echo by immediate reflection but rather was equipped with a hydrophone and tape recorder so that the pulse was stored on tape. Suppose that at some later time this recording was played back into the water. The compression would occur during both reception and rebroadcast of the sound waves, since in both cases the submarine would be moving relative to the water. Now suppose that the delay between recording and playback is made less and less. Nothing we do while shortening the delay time would affect the compression of the train of sound waves, so that there will still be *two* such compressions regardless of whether the delay is long or short. If the delay is very short, it approaches zero, and zero delay brings us back to the original situation of immediate reflection. Thus the porpoise hears the echo as 2000 waves occupying only about 147 meters. To be sure, one can split hairs and say that $150 \times 149/150 \times 149/150 \times 149/150$ are a very little more than 147. But it is not much more, and I promised to keep our arithmetic as simple as possible.

Finally the 2000 sound waves reach the receiving hydrophone of the sonar ship, which is still advancing at 10 meters per second to meet them, and the same compression is repeated for the last time. The end result is that the receiving circuit of the sonar system gets the 2000 waves in a shorter time than was required to send them out. The amount of this shortening is $0.1 - 0.1\left(\frac{149}{150}\right)^4$, or approximately 0.03 second.

The Doppler effect can be somewhat simplified by considering only the relative motion of the sonar system and its target; in this example the two were approaching at 20 meters per second. The pulse length of the received echo is then reduced by the square of the ratio of the relative velocity of approach to the velocity of sound. It is obvious that if the two ships were moving away from each other, the Doppler effect would work in the opposite direction, and the net effect would be a reduction in the frequency of the echo.

To return to our specific example, the final echo has a frequency at the sonar ship of $20{,}000 \times (\frac{150}{149})^4$, or about 20,540 c.p.s. If this is translated into an audible ping by combining it with a local frequency of 19,000 c.p.s., the echo beat note will be 1540 c.p.s., whereas if both ships were stationary, the beat note would be 1000 c.p.s. This is a fairly extreme example of rapid approach of the two ships, but in actual practice sonar operators can tell when a submarine turns or even when it speeds up or slows down. Though we understand far less of what goes on in a bat or porpoise brain than we know about the operation of this sonar system, it is reasonable to infer that similar comparisons of outgoing and echo frequencies may well be used to detect the motion of flying insects or swimming fish. The horseshoe bats with their constant frequency pulses can perhaps make better use of the Doppler effect than can the FM bats, but even the latter seem to use less frequency sweep when closing on insect prey than during cruising flights when they are presumably seeking to make their initial contact and detection.

Prospecting by Echo

Sound waves are not limited to air and water; they can also travel through solid materials of any kind. Even the echo sounder designed only to echolocate the bottom may sometimes show a type of false bottom different from the fish echoes or deep scattering layer described earlier. Sometimes the records indicate a second or third bottom *below* the real one rather than above it. This means that after the bottom echo of the probing pulse has returned to the ship's hull a further echo returns somewhat later. On first seeing such a record, an experienced physicist might surmise that the pulse had made two round trips through the depth of water under the ship's hull–down to the bottom, up to the surface, down to the bottom again, and finally back as a second echo. This can indeed happen, but then the time of arrival of the second echo is almost exactly twice that required by the first. Many of the false bottoms that seem to lie below the real bottom result from echoes returning at other times than twice the travel time of the first, direct echo. What really happens under certain conditions is that some of the sound energy penetrates into the mud or sand of the ocean floor, travels downward through it, and is then reflected back again by some sudden discontinuity such as a layer of rock of different hardness or density. Making due allowances for the velocity of sound transmission through the material just below the bottom of the ocean, geologists can estimate rather accurately the depth below the bottom at which this discontinuity occurs. Without even intending to do so, designers and users of echo sounders have thus hit upon a method of echolocation underground.

Quite purposefully and for many years, other geologists have been studying the transmission of sound waves through miles of the earth's crust. Earthquakes produce vibrations that can be detected by delicate vibration detectors known as seismographs. So do man-made explosions if they are sufficiently violent. Blasting in mines and quarries can be detected miles away, and the seismographic detection of nuclear explosions has now become a matter of major importance, a hotly debated issue at international conferences. By comparing the vibration records resulting from earthquakes at different points around the world, it is possible to deduce that some waves travel close to the surface, others through deeper layers of rock, while still others travel hundreds of miles below the surface. Careful study of the times of arrival of such waves at different listening stations has enabled geologists to learn much more than they could have determined by any other method about the composition of our planet. (The Science Study book *How Old Is the Earth* goes into this subject in more detail.)

The actual waves recorded by a seismograph are of quite low frequency, and they are usually so irregular that it is difficult or even meaningless to describe them in terms of frequencies. Major components vary from about 0.5 to 5 c.p.s. They also differ from sound waves in air or water in that they involve motion in directions other than the direction of wave propagation. There are several different types of seismic waves, classified according to the relative degrees of motion in various directions. By painstaking analysis of recordings made at various points above and below the ground and in different directions from the place of a test explosion, geologists can locate many kinds of rock structures below the surface. This procedure has been of great use in prospecting for oil, or rather for the types of rock and salt deposits that are commonly associated with it. Much of our industrial economy has been made possible by the success of this method for echolocating oil.

Echoes versus X-rays

Sound waves have also come into widespread use for harmless testing of materials such as metals and rubber. If the material is pure and homogeneous, it transmits sound waves in a smooth and orderly way. But if there are discontinuities, such as air bubbles in castings or defects in tire casings, they distort transmitted sound waves. In some cases very short pulses of sound are used to produce distinct echoes in the material being tested. The sound frequencies are often very high, up to 1 megacycle per second (10^6 c.p.s.), and this is possible because relatively short distances of transmission are involved. It is a comparatively inexpensive method of testing compared to structural failure of an important and costly machine, and the material is not damaged in any way.

Recently this sort of acoustic probing has been applied to the living bodies of animals and men. It is possible to detect discontinuities in our internal organs in this way, using sound waves generated at the surface of the body by suitable sound sources, such as crystals which are vibrated at high frequencies by electric currents. This method is not without its dangers, for intense sound waves in our bodies can produce damage. But, when properly controlled, the method has some advantages over X-rays. At least any damage is local and, insofar as we know, is not a long-delayed effect on our genes—the complex molecules in our reproductive organs, some of which may in time determine what our children will be like. One limitation of this method stems from the large number of discontinuities that are naturally present in a human body—those between muscle and bone, digestive tract and blood vessels, heart and lungs, etc. Thus any abnormalities must be discriminated from a complex background of natural structures, and this makes it more difficult to locate a tumor in a human brain than an air bubble in a cast-iron pipe. Nevertheless, this new means for studying our invisible insides may lead in time to safer or more effective methods of locating internal disorders in an early and curable stage. The discrimination problems may be no more difficult than those facing a blind man or a bat, and human ingenuity may eventually solve this type of problem along with the others mentioned in previous chapters.

Radar

The detection of distant aircraft by echoes of radio waves stands as one of mankind's major technical accomplishments. In military results alone it has well repaid the billions of dollars spent on its development and on manufacture of military radar systems. Not only can ground- or ship-based radar systems detect airplanes at hundreds of miles but smaller radars carried on airplanes can locate other aircraft and also resolve a surprising amount of detail on the ground below. Radar systems developed for the purpose can draw crude but highly useful maps of hundreds of square miles of terrain in a fraction of a second. The maps are drawn on specialized cathode-ray oscilloscope screens. Radar echoes can also be used to locate and track clouds and storms, birds and locusts, meteors, earth satellites, and ballistic missiles. Shortly after World War II, radar echoes were successfully detected from the moon. In 1958, for the first time, very faint echoes from the planet Venus were detected. Although this book cannot discuss radar thoroughly, certain basic similarities are well worth considering, and it is even possible to make a rough comparison of the performance and efficiencies of radar systems and natural living systems that have evolved to enable bats to navigate and catch insects in the dark.

Relative Efficiency of Bats and Radar

As with the sonar system we discussed, this comparison will be based on radar systems that served well in

World War II and have since been retired to pasture—replaced by somewhat more efficient models. To make the comparison more meaningful, I have selected a typical airborne radar set which was a real triumph of engineering skill in that it accomplished, with a relatively small weight and power consumption, as much as many previous models that were far bulkier and less efficient. This radar operated at a frequency of 9375 megacycles ($\lambda = \frac{3 \times 10^{10}}{9.375 \times 10^{9}}$), or a wave length of 3.2 centimeters. While this frequency is vastly higher than those used by bats, porpoises, or naval sonar systems, the wave length is not greatly different because of the much higher velocity of light or other electromagnetic radiation. Where our sonar system emitted its acoustic signals at a peak power level of 600 watts, this radar developed a peak power of 10,000 watts. It is important to stress that none of these systems, living or instrumental, emits power continuously; all have a relatively low duty cycle, or ratio of time on to time off. In typical operation this radar emitted pulses lasting 0.8 microsecond (8×10^{-7} second) at a pulse repetition rate of 810 pulses per second. In other words, every 1/810th second, or 1.23×10^{-3} second it emitted a pulse lasting 8×10^{-7} second, followed by a silent interval about 1500 times as long. This left ample time for echoes to return (at the velocity of light) before the next pulse arrived. The entire radar system weighed 124 pounds, but this does not include the weight of the airplane generator which supplied the electric power. This radar set detected aircraft at 50 miles under most conditions and was a brilliant operational success. It is therefore of some interest to inquire how well it compares with bat systems, watt for watt of power emitted and gram for gram of weight.

This comparison is not a simple one because of the

widely different circumstances in which the two classes of echo-ranging systems are actually used. Bats are interested in detecting small insects at a few feet or yards. The user of an airborne radar wishes to locate objects on the ground and other airplanes some miles away. Bats use sound waves, while radar employs radio waves of only slightly greater wave lengths. Bats maneuver very rapidly, the whole sequence of detection, turning toward an insect, intercepting, catching, and swallowing, all occurring within 1 second. In ordinary use of an airborne radar, the operator sees a spot on his oscilloscope screen, notes how it changes in position relative to his own flight path, and then takes appropriate action. This may vary all the way from a turn to avoid any danger of collision, if the two airplanes are airliners, to a close pursuit and firing of a machine gun or rocket at the other plane if it is an enemy in time of war. In both cases the whole operation may be accomplished by a man sitting in a darkened cabin looking only at spots on his radar screen. The bat does it all within one second, in the dark, with a brain smaller than the eraser on a pencil.

To make comparison a quantitative one, we can best tabulate the important quantities which are known for the two systems and on which we may base estimates of their relative efficiencies. The table on page 123 gives approximately the range of the radar and also its weight and power requirements. An efficient system for echolocation should detect the smallest possible objects at the greatest possible distances and it should do so with the least possible power and the lightest possible apparatus. Bulky installations of whirling machinery may be impressive at first glance, but unnecessary complexity and power expenditure are actually signs of inefficiency. With this in mind, let us set up an efficiency index, an equation which will evaluate the combination of these four important factors. Such an index should have a high value for the most efficient systems and should be roughly proportional to the relative efficiencies of the various systems of echolocation that we compare. As will become clear a little later, this is not as simple as it might seem, but the process of attempting to define such an index, and then modifying it as may seem necessary, will in itself prove to be helpful in calling attention to the various quantitative considerations that are important for echolocation.

TABULAR COMPARISONS OF BATS AND RADAR

	AN/APS − 10 radar system	Big brown bat	Little brown bat
Target detected	Airplane	Insect	Wire
Target diameter, d (cm)	300	1	1.8×10^{-2}
Range of detection, R (cm)	8×10^{6}	200	90
Weight of apparatus, W (grams)	9×10^{4}	1	0.5
Emitted power, P (watts)	10^{4}	10^{-5}	10^{-6}
R/PWd	2.9×10^{-5}	2×10^{7}	10^{10}
R^4/PWd^2	5×10^{13}	1.6×10^{14}	3.8×10^{16}
R^4/PWd^4	5.5×10^{8}	1.6×10^{14}	1.2×10^{21}

The above table lists the range of detection, R, the diameter of the target, d (both in centimeters), the power emission, P (watts), and the weight of the system, W (grams). For the bats, 10 per cent of the weight of a fasting animal seems a generous allowance for the lar-

ynx, ears, auditory portions of the brain, and the othe
parts used directly for echolocation. For both bat an
radar the power is the peak level reached during eac
pulse. It may be recalled from Chapter 2 that the ears o
bats and men operate at sound power levels ranging fron
about 10^{-16} to 10^{-4} watt per square centimeter. The airborne radar detection of another airplane at 50 miles i
compared with two cases of echolocation by bats—th
detection of a 1-centimeter insect (or pebble) by a bi
brown bat at 2 meters, and the echolocation of a 0.18
millimeter wire by a little brown bat at 90 centimeters

The first approach to defining the efficiency inde
might be simply to have R, the distance of detection
in the numerator, and the other three quantities,
(power), W (weight), and d (target size), in the de
nominator, where large values will tend to lower the in
dex. This index, R/PWd, is listed in the next row of th
table, and when judged on this basis, the bats appear bil
lions of times better than the radar system. But a littl
reflection shows that, in defining the index in this way
we have made an important assumption; namely, tha
these four quantities are really related to one another a
we have entered them in the equation. For example
this definition of efficiency assumes that range will in
crease in direct proportion to power. But for all rada
systems, and probably all bats, the emitted energy fall
off as the square of the distance. And most small target
send back echoes that also obey the inverse-square law
As a result of these geometrical relationships, whic
apply to all types of wave motion including both ligh
and sound, the energy in echoes returning from object
at a considerable distance is proportional to $1/R^4$. Thi
means that to obtain twice the range a system o
echolocation will need 2^4, or 16 times as much powe
and we should therefore change our index to contain

to the fourth power instead of the first. This will greatly increase the rating scored by the radar set detecting an airplane at 50 miles.

Having made this improvement in the index, we should also scrutinize the other variables in our equation, in particular the size of the target, d. If a series of targets is fairly large relative to the wave length of the signal being used to generate an echo, the echo power is usually proportional roughly to their areas, or to d^2. This is true of most radar targets, and certainly of airplanes being echolocated with 3.2-centimeter waves. Is it also true for bats? The insects they catch vary from somewhat below one wave length to several wave lengths, and of course the FM bats employ orientation sounds containing a whole octave of frequencies, or a twofold range of wave lengths in each pulse. It is probably reasonable to assume that in insect detection the echo power varies as the square of the target diameter, although in some cases the insects may be enough below one wave length so that this assumption would lead to an overestimate of the echo strength. The next line of the table therefore lists for each of the three systems the value of the revised efficiency index, R^4/PWd^2. Even on this basis the bats are somewhat superior to the radar.

Finally, we should pay a little more attention to the bats which detect wires far smaller than one wave length, such as the little brown bat listed in the third row of the table. When wires or other cylindrical obstacles are much smaller than one wave length, the echo power varies as d^4, and the 0.18-millimeter wires detected at 90 centimeters are certainly in this size range. This domain of target size produces what is sometimes called *Rayleigh scattering,* after the nineteenth-century physicist who analyzed it with special reference to light scattered by tiny particles in the air. Such light makes up most of what we see in the sky, and since the particles are of less than the wave lengths of visible light (4 to 7×10^{-5} centimeter), short wave length light is more strongly scattered than other colors. This is why the sky is blue. By analogy we might say that the bat flying up to these wires must hear "blue echoes." In any event, a case could be made for evaluating bat sonar by means of an index containing d^4 rather than d or d^2, and the value of R^4/PWd^4 is therefore listed in the last line of the table.

The drastic results of changing the definition of our efficiency index should now be clear. This may indeed open serious questions as to whether such different systems for echolocation can be meaningfully compared on a simple numerical basis. Furthermore, several other important factors have not yet been brought into the comparison. Bats operating with sound waves in air face serious reductions in echo signal due to the absorption of sound in air, especially at higher frequencies. During the round trip from bat to target and return, sound of 50 kc loses power by a factor of 0.63 for every meter of distance, in addition to the reduction due to the inverse fourth power reduction for echoes. At 100 kc the reduction is by a factor of 0.44 over every meter. Radio waves suffer no such severe losses in traveling through the air. This fact puts the bat at a great disadvantage over long distances. On the other hand, there is a consideration which would favor most radar systems as compared to bats. This is the duty cycle, or fraction of the time during which energy is being emitted. In typical cases, such as those included in our table, a bat would be emitting 10 to 20 pulses per second, each pulse lasting 2 to 5 milliseconds, so that the duty cycle would vary between 0.02 and 0.1. The radar had a far lower duty cycle, however, the interval between pulses having been about 1500 times as long as the pulse itself, so that the duty cycle would be about 0.0007. This means that if we were to use average power rather than peak power in our comparison, the bats would suffer by a factor of about 100. Yet a partisan of the bats might offer in rebuttal the consideration that we allowed 10 per cent of the animal's weight for its sonar apparatus, whereas the weight of the radar set was a much smaller fraction of the mass of the airplane that carried it. From the bat's point of view it would perhaps be more valid to compare its whole weight with that of the entire airplane.

If we take the broadest view, it is obvious that bats and other living animals are vastly more efficient than radars and airplanes, even though it is difficult to attach numbers to the comparison. Bats maintain and repair their living machinery; airplanes and radar sets must be manufactured and repaired by men. Bats catch and digest all the food that provides power for their bodily mechanisms; airplanes are not expected to refuel by catching birds, and the fuel pumped to them requires no chemical processing in the plane before use. Nor do any artifical mechanisms reproduce themselves. The unusual aspect of the comparison we have been making is that a living mechanism can be compared directly with a radar set on almost the same terms that an engineer would employ in comparing one radar with another. The results of the comparison inspire a healthy respect for the mechanisms of flesh and blood which have evolved in nature under the pressure of natural selection.

CHAPTER 6

Suppose You Were Blind

In the preceding chapters we have examined waves and echoes to understand better how animals and men have used them to locate objects which are essential for survival. Such studies of natural phenomena often seem useless to all but a very few people, but so do many scientific explorations. Yet history has clearly shown that men have improved their lot by investigations into the unknown. However insignificant it may have seemed at the time, there is a true inner satisfaction in discovering new relationships and new information to add to our understanding of the world around us. We often hope that observations and new facts can one day be used to improve our environment still further. What could be more beneficial than trying to apply this new-found knowledge to men who cannot see with their eyes? Can we help them to "see" with their ears—to learn the language of echoes?

Blindness is always a tragedy for human beings because our brains and our whole way of life are built around light and vision. But men's eyes are not their only channels of communication with the rest of the world, and sound is in some ways even more useful. For example, we can see somewhat less than 1 octave of frequencies, or wave lengths, roughly from 4 to 7.5×10^{-5} meters. Our sense of hearing, on the other hand, extends from about 20 to 20,000 c.p.s., a range of a thousandfold, or approximately 10 octaves. Audible sound can thus contain a much richer variety of frequencies than visible light, and this is partly why sound rather than light is used for speech. Of course, there are other reasons; for instance, living organisms cannot generate light, except for a few luminescent animals and plants.

The sharp shadows cast by light make it less useful as a vehicle for speech and short-range communication. Just because sound does go around corners, it is useful in calling and signaling, particularly when almost every motion and contact between a person or animal and the physical world around it generates some sound. The great advantage of light to us is that it has short wave lengths and, consequently, objects of small size give off specular reflections. It is for this reason that eyes and lenses can focus sharp images. Only when one tries to use a microscope to see objects about the size of the wave length of light does that wave length become an important limitation. An object must be smaller than one micron (one millionth of a meter) before it scatters light rather than reflecting it.

If sound waves and light waves did not already exist, we well might find scientists trying to invent them, one to form sharp images and permit accurate observations of small details, the other with a wide-frequency spectrum to convey complex information with a minimum of interference from shadow-casting obstacles. The two types complement each other, and while the loss of our sense organs for either is a major handicap, there is enough duplication of what each can do to permit some substitution of one after losing the other.

The Sense of Obstacles

Blindness has been an all-too-common affliction of men, and while no device or procedure can completely replace lost sight, blind men for centuries have learned to get about in the world and carry on a surprising number of activities. Some become so skillful at avoiding obstacles and maintaining an adequate general orientation that it is difficult for a stranger to realize they are really blind. For example, there was once a blind boy who learned when six years old to ride his tricycle all about the sidewalks near his home without injury or accident. When he approached pedestrians, he steered around them, and he always knew when to turn corners without going into the street. Other blind people travel widely in busy cities, crossing streets, using buses and trains, dodging lampposts and wire fences. How do they detect these obstacles before touching them? Many theories have been advanced, both by the blind people themselves and by those who have worked or lived with them. Curiously enough, the most skillful of the blind differ widely in their explanations of their own abilities. Many say they feel with their hands or faces the proximity of obstacles, and the term "facial vision" has come into wide use to describe their orientation to objects which are too far away to feel or touch. Others believe that hearing is somehow involved; still others speak of "pressures" and other ill-defined sensations that warn them of dangers just ahead.

The central question is obviously the nature of the physical message that travels from the obstacles to the blind man, and the way in which his remaining sense organs detect and interpret this information from the outside world. From about 1890 to 1940 many studies were made of the "sense of obstacles," but only in the early 1940s was a conclusive answer obtained from carefully controlled experiments. While these experiments were performed by men who called themselves psychologists, the experiments can be considered classic examples of *biophysics,* the application to problems posed by living organisms of the same basic principles of investigation that have developed physics as a rigorous science. The chief difference between biophysics, thus broadly defined, and the physics of non-living systems is the greater degree of complexity and refinement of living organisms. Animals and men are made of far more intricate mechanisms than clickers and ripple tanks, microscopes or television sets, and this is why our understanding of biological processes is so much less thorough and complete than our knowledge of physics or chemistry.

The psychologists, or biophysicists, who finally solved the question of obstacle perception by the blind were Professor Karl M. Dallenbach of Cornell University, and two graduate students, one of whom, Michael Supa, was himself totally blind. Milton Cotzin, the other student, had normal vision, but he and others who served as experimental subjects wore blindfolds for many hours at a time in order to experience what life is like for the blind, and, in particular, to develop as much as possible the ability to detect obstacles before bumping into them. First the experimenters set up a sort of obstacle course, a long hallway down which the subject walked and across which was placed a large screen of fiberboard at some point chosen by the experimenter. This location was varied from trial to trial, so that the subject never knew whether it was 6, 10, 18, 24, or 30 feet ahead of the starting point, or even whether it was there at all. His task was to walk along the hallway, say when he first thought he was approaching the screen, and then walk up as close as he could without striking it.

Some of the subjects, both blind and blindfolded, could judge accurately the presence or absence of the screen at several feet and then move in until their faces were within a few inches before deciding that any further approach would bring them into contact with it. The phenomenon of obstacle detection was thus brought into the laboratory in a manner which allowed it to be studied repeatedly under reasonably constant conditions. This step is often a crucial one in attacking scientific problems of this sort. Elusive and unpredictable events are very much more difficult to study than those which can be repeated under known conditions. Only in the latter case is it fairly easy to vary the factors that seem likely to be important and then observe the results. Earlier studies of obstacle detection by the blind had been plagued with great variability in the performance of the subjects. That mainly is why they had not led to clear and decisive answers. Yet Supa, Cotzin, and Dallenbach built their experimental design on the extensive, if inconclusive, experience of earlier experimenters. Without this background they would probably not have been able to devise such decisive experiments.

Once they had arranged conditions where blind or blindfolded people were regularly detecting a standardized test obstacle, the next step was the theoretically obvious but nevertheless rather difficult one of eliminating one possible channel of sensory communication at a time, while leaving the subject with free use of the others. One leading theory was that the skin supplied some kind of sensation of touch or pressure when obstacles were nearby; another was that sound played a major role. The practical problem in testing the "skin pressure theory" was to shield the subjects' skin from any possible influence that might be arriving from the obstacle, and this was doubly difficult because no one could say what this might be—air currents, electromagnetic radiation, heat or cold, or possibly some sort of energy not known to physics. To test the sound theory, the logical procedure was to prevent sounds from reaching the subjects' ears without interfering with whatever the skin might be feeling as a result of proximity to the obstacles. The covering of the skin clearly had to be accomplished without interfering with the subjects' hearing, and vice versa. The final outfit that the subjects were obliged to wear consisted of a long veil of thick felt which covered the head and shoulders, plus heavy leather gloves to shield the hands. Ordinary clothing covered the rest of the body surface. Such was the protection that they could not feel even the air current of an electric fan directed at their heads. After some preliminary trials to accustom them to walking about in this "armor," the subjects found they could detect the screen almost as well as ever. The average distance of first detection had been 6.9 feet with no veil or gloves, and it was now reduced only slightly —to 5.25 feet. This seemed to dispose of the possibility that obstacles were detected by feeling them through the skin, despite the fact that originally some of this group of subjects, like many blind people, were certain that they *felt* the obstacles with the hands or face.

The next experiment was to leave the hands and face completely free but to cover the subjects' ears. Earlier experiments of this kind had given conflicting results; sometimes the detection of obstacles was impaired, sometimes not. Complete exclusion of sound by earplugs is not possible, but Supa, Cotzin, and Dallenbach wished to be sure that as little sound as possible reached their subjects. They therefore wore earplugs of wax and cotton, ear muffs, and padding over the sides of the head. This compound series of barriers was necessary because many sounds, particularly those of low frequency, penetrate ordinary earplugs or ear muffs. Everyone knows from the ordinary experience of wearing ear muffs or parka hoods in cold weather that by speaking slightly louder than usual one can still converse with his companions no matter how well the ears are protected from the winter winds.

So thorough was this muffling that the subjects could not hear the sounds of their own footsteps, and instructions could only be given them by loud shouts. A loud shout can easily have 10^9 times the energy of a barely audible whisper. Direct measurement of the intensity necessary for them to detect a test sound showed that their auditory sensitivity had been reduced by a factor of about 4,000,000; that is, they could hear the test sound only after its energy level had been increased four millionfold above the level that was just audible without the ear covering.

When the same subjects were now asked to repeat the experiments with their hearing thus impaired, the results were spectacular. None retained any obstacle-detection ability at all, and in each of one hundred trials every subject bumped unexpectedly into the screen. One of the blind men, who had stoutly maintained that sound played no part at all in his "facial vision," complained that he was now getting no sensation at all, and for the first time he walked hesitantly and held out his hands to guard against anticipated accidents. If sound does account for the obstacle-detection ability, one might ask why there was any reduction in distance of first detection when the subjects wore the felt veil and leather gloves.

This was probably due to the reduction in sound level caused by the shielding effect of the bulky hood.

Guiding Echoes

These experiments would seem to have settled the matter once and for all, but criticisms would still have been possible if the experimenters had stopped at this point. Perhaps the pressure of the ear covering was disturbing some subtle tactile sense. Perhaps blind men were warned of obstacles not by hearing as such but by some special kind of pressure sense involving the ear canal or adjacent areas of skin. Even men who had studied this subject for years were skeptical that sound waves could be the messengers by which blind people detected obstacles. Further, many blind men themselves still continued to think they *felt* obstacles. To convince such skeptics it was necessary to modify the experiment so that sound and only sound carried the necessary information from the outside world into the subject's nervous system. This might seem a hopeless task; if the experiments described above were unconvincing, what arguments could hope to overcome such skepticism?

The answer was to employ a telephone system to transmit the appropriate sounds to the subject sitting in a remote and soundproof room. The sounds transmitted over the telephone wires were those picked up by a microphone carried by a man walking along the same obstacle course. They were similar, though not identical, to what the man would hear himself if he were listening for evidence that the screen was just ahead.

The results of the telephone experiment were astonishingly close to those obtained by the same subjects in the original tests. They could sit in the soundproof room and decide by listening to the telephone whether the screen was being approached or not. After some practice they could detect the screen at an average distance of 6.4 feet, only a little less than their average of 6.9 feet when they were doing their own walking and listening. Such a result would seem to dispel all doubts; surely no one could argue now that anything but sound was involved. But scientists who have studied problems like this have learned to be extremely cautious. Many experiments which have seemed this convincing have turned out to be misleading. Suppose, for example, that the person who walked up to the screen with the microphone changed his breathing rhythm or the sounds of his footsteps and thus unconsciously conveyed to the remote listener his proximity to the screen? This sort of unconscious signaling has been known to occur, and, incidentally, it accounts for many cases of what has been interpreted as mental telepathy.

This worry led to further experiments in which the second person was replaced by a motor-driven cart which carried the microphone towards the screen. The subject in the soundproof room controlled the movements of the cart while listening to the sounds the microphone picked up. As often happens in a scientific experiment, new facts raise new questions–one often ends up with more questions than he had at the beginning. Here the question raised was of major importance. Granted that sounds could be conveyed over the telephone system, what were the actual sounds that told the listener the screen was near? In the original experiment no special effort was made to generate sounds or produce echoes; indeed, the experimenters in the beginning had been uncertain that sounds were really of any consequence. They had simply tried to bring phenomenon into the laboratory and arrange conditions under which it could be repeatedly studied. But having learned that sound, rather than anything which could not travel along telephone wires, informed the blind man that the screen was in front of him, the experimenters had to consider the nature of these sounds.

Footsteps were an obvious possibility, and when the original experiments were repeated with the subjects walking in their stocking feet on a soft carpet, their ability to detect the screen was greatly reduced. The average distance of first detection fell from 6.9 feet when the subjects were wearing shoes and walking on the bare floor to 3.4 feet when the sounds of their footsteps were dampened by the carpet. Some subjects snapped their fingers or made clucking sounds, but others apparently relied on whatever sounds were present in the hallway, such as the sound of their own breathing or the rustle of their clothing. This question had not been seriously considered in the design of the first experiments, but now that the investigation had reached the point where the microphone was to be mounted on a cart there would be no sound from footsteps or breathing. Some other sound had to be substituted, which provided the opportunity to study the usefulness of various sounds in providing audible clues to the presence or absence of obstacles. Obviously, too, the experiment involved echoes. If some sound told a listener that the screen was present, it must have been a sound which was different with the screen than without it.

In order to study the character of the echoes used by blind people, the experimenters then equipped the cart with a loudspeaker as well as a microphone. A variety of sounds with known characteristics could now be generated by the loudspeaker for further tests. If a loud hissing noise was used–that is, a noise containing a wide range of audible frequencies–the screen could be detected by the subjects listening to the telephone in the soundproof room. The distance of first detection averaged 3.75 feet, less than the range of detection when in an earlier test a person carried the microphone toward the screen. Nevertheless, it was an impressive performance, considering how greatly the situation had been altered from the first series of experiments. Other sounds were also tried, but the experiments were concluded before the ideal sound had been discovered which men might use to obtain the more revealing echoes. The investigations ended because the original problem had been conclusively solved by the proof that sounds and, in particular, echoes were the messages that inform blind men about the existence and position of obstacles.

One significant feature of this important discovery is the striking divergence between the subjective feelings of many blind people and all the objective evidence which we have examined. When a man has developed the remarkable ability to find his way about through the bustling traffic of a modern city in what to him is total darkness, and when he does this so skillfully and unobtrusively that one can travel with him for hours and never suspect that he is blind, then it is natural to assume that he knows what he is doing and how he does it. But often the expert blind man can say only that he somehow "feels" his way and "knows" before he bumps into the tree or fence post that it is there. If questioned more closely, he may say he feels the proximity of the object with his hands, his face, or his forehead. Yet when the process of obstacle detection is studied under controlled conditions, it is clear that sounds and hearing are the essential ingredients. In addition, the whole surface of the blind man's skin can be covered by heavy felt or leather without preventing him from detecting obstacles before he strikes them. When his ears are plugged, he no longer "feels" the obstacles with his hands or face, and if he continues on his way, he invariably strikes them without warning. Subjective impressions obviously can be misleading–we do not always know just which of our senses is informing us about our surroundings. This is not to say that our senses are not keen, but rather that our conscious thinking about them may lead us to the wrong conclusion about how they operate.

This is not a unique misapprehension concerning the workings of our sense organs, although perhaps it is an extreme one. Another example also involves the sense of hearing. How do we know where a sound is coming from? Sometimes we see the source and are thus informed of its position, but everyone is able to locate the origin of an unfamiliar sound heard in darkness, and usually with great accuracy. Sometimes we locate a sound source approximately by turning our heads until the sound is louder in one ear than in the other, but more often and with great precision we rely on the difference in the same sound as it arrives at the two ears. Consider for the present only one type of sound, a sharp click. The most important property of the bundle of sound waves constituting the click is the time of arrival of the first sound waves at the two ears. If the click comes from straight ahead, the two ears receive the first sound waves at exactly the same time because they are equidistant from the source. If, however, the click arises at some point to the right of the direction you are facing, it reaches the right ear a small fraction of a second sooner than the left. If the source is 90° to one side, the opposite ear is about 20 centimeters farther away than the closer one, and since sound waves in air travel about 30 centimeters per millisecond, this means that the maximum possible difference in time of arrival at the two ears is less than 1 millisecond. Yet such is the precision of the auditory portions of our brains that we can easily distinguish between a sound source that is straight ahead and one that is displaced only 10° to one side. If the source is 3 meters away, the 10° displacement which is clearly noticeable involves a difference in time of arrival at our two ears of about 0.1 millisecond. It is difficult

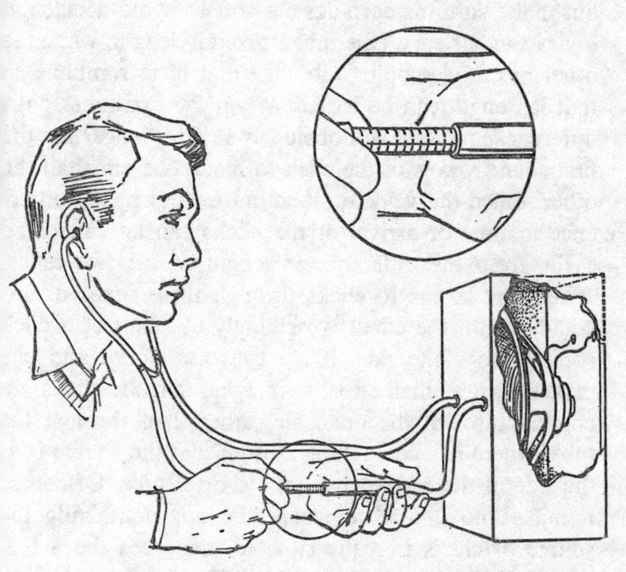

Fig. 15. Your ability to discriminate minute differences in the time of arrival of two sounds can be tested with this device. Any sound source will do, such as a small transistor radio, if tightly enclosed in the box so that you hear it only through the tubes.

to locate sound sources accurately if they lie directly in front of us, or anywhere in the plane that is equidistant from the two ears. If we have to attempt this, we usually do so by moving our heads about and bringing one ear closer to the source.

The role of differences in time of arrival of a click at

the two ears can be studied with the aid of a simple device illustrated in Fig. 15. This consists of a source of clicks, which could be a loudspeaker or a mechanical clicker, and a sound-tight box to house it. From the box lead two tubes each ending like a physician's stethoscope, but make sure the earplugs are soft to avoid accidental injury to your ears. One tube is fixed in length, while the other has a telescoping tube like that of a trombone so that its length can be varied. When the two tubes have different lengths, it will obviously require longer for the first sound waves of the click to reach one ear than the other. Since the velocity of sound is known, the difference in time of arrival of the clicks can be calculated easily from the difference in length of the two tubes. When one listens to clicks through these tubes of unequal length, the effect is strikingly like that of a click coming from one side. If the eyes are closed and one makes even a small effort to imagine that the clicks are coming through the open air rather than through the tubes, there is a compelling illusion that the source is at the side of the ear receiving the shorter tube. Of course it makes no difference where the box containing the source of clicks is really situated, nor does the actual length of the two tubes matter. When precise measurements are made with more refined apparatus of this same type, the minimum time difference that leads to this illusion of a source at one side or the other is less than 0.1 millisecond.

We need experiments like these to tell us about one of the principal ways in which we locate the source of a sound. We never think, "That click reached my right ear 1/10,000 second before it got to my left ear; therefore, it must have come from a little to one side of the median plane of my head." We simply recognize that the click came from one side without any idea how we located it. In much the same way, a blind man learns to anticipate collisions with obstacles under certain conditions, usually without realizing at all that these conditions are the presence of audible echoes. Recognizing the proximity of an obstacle and knowing from experience the pain of bumping into it, he comes to believe that he felt its nearness with his hands or face. All this adds up to a warning not to interpret the workings of our sense organs and our brains too hastily; they may be operating in other ways than we are first inclined to think. But we should not go to the other extreme and conclude that measuring instruments will always improve upon our unaided senses. As we have learned, sense organs and brains of men, porpoises, bats, and beetles accomplish extremely difficult feats of detection and discrimination.

To return to the blind man's problems of orientation, echolocation is certainly the technique by which skillful blind people find their way in the "dark." But with the general question thus answered, we are immediately impelled to ask what type of sound will provide a blind man with the most informative echoes. In the final experiments by Supa, Cotzin, and Dallenbach where the cart carried the loudspeaker and microphone up to the test obstacle, it turned out that a hissing noise was more effective than pure tones. But the average distance of detection was only 3.75 feet instead of 6.9. Does this mean that footsteps are more efficient sounds for this purpose, or does it mean that the cart with the loudspeaker and microphone was less easily controlled by the remote listener? From the experiments described in Chapters 2 and 3 it is clear that some sounds generate more useful echoes than others, and that a very short click has the advantage that it ends before the first echo begins to return. But footsteps on the floor are not especially sharp clicks, even when the walker's shoes have hard soles. Some blind men prefer shoes with metal heel plates, perhaps because of the sharper footsteps that result. If you have carried out some experiments with clickers, like the one illustrated in Fig. 7, it must be obvious that if you, a rank beginner, can detect trees, an experienced blind man can do at least as well. In recent laboratory experiments blind or blindfolded subjects have learned to distinguish between wooden disks held a foot or two in front of their faces. Size differences as small as 10 per cent can be distinguished by especially skillful subjects under favorable conditions and after considerable practice.

But we can properly ask whether footsteps, cane taps, or even toy clickers mounted in horns are really the best types of sound for a blind man's purposes. Do they generate the most informative possible echoes or are there other types of sound that would be superior? The question is simply asked, but the search for a convincing answer has been difficult and frustrating. Various types of clickers and portable sound sources have been built and tested. Some, particularly the directional clickers, have been used extensively by a small number of blind men, including their inventors. But the results have been far from satisfactory, and many users find it too difficult to hear consistent echoes or find the added facility at orientation not worth the embarrassment caused by a conspicuous audible sound that calls attention to their handicap. Yet almost every object that a blind man needs to detect does interact in some way with audible sound waves. This being so, why can we not devise a probing sound which will produce audible echoes that are recognizably related to the objects a blind man needs to locate?

One difficulty has already been called to our attention in the experiment where tape recordings of clicks or other impulsive sounds were played backward on a tape recorder. This experiment demonstrated the effectiveness of our built-in suppressor mechanism which renders echoes far less audible because our ears are temporarily insensitive immediately after a loud outgoing sound. A multitude of echoes are clearly audible on reversed playback when they precede a sharp click or pistol shot, but are quite unnoticed when they follow the louder sound as they do in ordinary life. Is this the major reason why blind men fail to learn as much from echoes as they theoretically should? And if so, could not some device be developed to overcome this difficulty? No one knows the answers to these questions, and they are good examples of the truism that no branch of science is complete or finished. Perhaps some reader may have the ideas and the opportunity to make further advances toward a real solution of the blind man's problems of orientation. Just because some men have failed so far to find such a solution, others should not be discouraged from new attempts, especially when the potential gains to human welfare are so great.

FURTHER READING

Barnes, H.: *Oceanography and Marine Biology.* London: George Allen and Unwin, Ltd., 1959.

This up-to-date elementary survey of oceanography includes a chapter on the sounds of marine animals and the use of sound for exploration of the ocean depths.

Boys, C. V.: *Soap Bubbles and the Forces Which Mould Them.* New York: Science Study Series, Doubleday Anchor Books, 1959.

A small readable classic of science which will give you, among other things, a better understanding of surface tension.

Bowen, E. G. (Editor): *A Textbook of Radar.* Cambridge, England: Cambridge University Press, 2nd Edition, 1954.

This textbook contains more general background material, including such fascinating subjects as radar echoes from the moon and the use of radar in navigation.

Buddenbrock, W. von: *The Senses.* Ann Arbor, Michigan: University of Michigan Press, 1958.

A readable and authoritative account of sense organs of all sorts of animals, from the eyes of scallops to inner ears of men.

Carthy, J. D.: *Animal Navigation.* London: Georg Allen and Unwin, Ltd., 1956.

This popular and readable book describes the orienta tion and navigation of insects, fishes, birds, and whale as well as those of bats and domestic animals.

Fletcher, H.: *Speech and Hearing in Communication* New York: Van Nostrand, 1953.

This thorough and somewhat technical book sum marizes the extensive researches carried out at the Be Telephone Laboratories and elsewhere on the physica properties of speech, the mechanisms of human hear ing, and the nature of hearing losses and deafness.

Griffin, D. R.: *Listening in the Dark.* New Haven, Con necticut: Yale University Press, 1958.

Many aspects of the natural sonar of bats, birds, an porpoises are discussed more fully than in this sho monograph, including the many different types of bat and their orientation sounds, their pursuit and captur of flying insects, fish, and other food. There ar chapters on echolocation by blind men, and on th acuity of echolocation achieved by bats, includin their ability to hear faint echoes despite the presenc of louder jamming noises.

Griffin, D. R.: "Bird Sonar." *Scientific American Maga zine,* March 1954.

"More about Bat 'Radar.'" *Scientific American Mag azine,* August 1958.

These articles contain excellent illustrations and sup plement the chapters of this monograph dealing wit the natural sonar of bats and birds.

Horton, J. W.: *Fundamentals of Sonar.* Annapolis Maryland: U. S. Naval Institute, 1957.

This rather technical book describes the basic principles and operation of electronic sonar systems as they are used on ships. It explains the Doppler effect and other basic phenomena of echolocation with special reference to underwater sound.

Iurley, P. M.: *How Old is the Earth.* New York: cience Study Series, Doubleday Anchor Books, 1959.

This modern book on radioactivity as an energy source in the earth and as means of measuring time also includes a piece on seismic waves.

ellogg, W. N.: *Porpoises and Sonar.* Chicago: Uniersity of Chicago Press, 1961.

An elementary account of the use of echolocation by marine mammals, and the types of experiment by which the acoustic orientation of these fascinating animals has been studied.

idenour, L. N. (Editor): *Radar System Engineering.* ew York: McGraw-Hill, 1st Edition, 1947.

This is a general description of the radar systems developed during World War II by the Radiation Laboratory at M.I.T. While parts of it are quite technical, many chapters can easily be understood by any seriously interested reader of this monograph. Radar sets and systems are described and illustrated in sufficient detail to permit, for example, the sort of comparison with biological systems that were discussed in Chapter 5.

oeder, K. D.: *Nerve Cells and Insect Behavior.* Camidge, Massachusetts: Harvard University Press, 1963.

An excellent summary of the experiments by which Roeder and Treat analyzed the countermeasures used by moths to escape from the bats that hunt them by echolocation, plus a fine introduction to neurophys ology.

van Bergeijk, Willem A.; Pierce, John R.; and Davi Edward E., Jr.: *Waves and the Ear*. New York: Sc ence Study Series, Doubleday Anchor Books, 1960.

A biologist and two scientist-engineers collaborate c an elementary but thorough discussion of sour waves and their interactions with the human nervo system.

Rummell, J. A.: "Modern Sonar Systems." *Electroni* (Engineering Edition), January 1958, pages 58–62.

A brief survey of the apparatus used in sonar system

Witcher, C. M., and Washington, L.: "Echo-Locatic for the Blind." *Electronics,* December 1954, pag 136–137.

A brief but complete description of one of the mo successful sound-generating devices used by blir people to find their way about. The late C. M Witcher was himself blind and he devoted his e gineering talents to improving such devices for h own use and for the benefit of other blind peopl

Zahl, P. A. (Editor): *Blindness*. Princeton, New Jerse Princeton University Press, 1950.

A collection of articles by different authors discussir the most important problems faced by blind pe ple, education for the blind, vocational rehabilitatio talking books, guide dogs, guidance devices, and th remote possibility of direct stimulation of the opt nerves or visual areas of the brain.

INDEX

INDEX

ANCHOR BOOKS

SCIENCE STUDY SERIES

ACCELERATORS–Robert R. Wilson and Raphael Littauer, S17
BIRD MIGRATION–Donald R. Griffin, S37
BIRTH OF A NEW PHYSICS–I. Bernard Cohen, S10
CLOUD PHYSICS AND CLOUD SEEDING–Louis J. Battan, S29
COMPUTERS AND THE HUMAN MIND: An Introduction to Artificial Intelligence–Donald G. Fink, S43
COUNT RUMFORD: PHYSICIST EXTRAORDINARY–Sanborn C. Brown, S28
CRYSTALS AND CRYSTAL GROWING–Alan Holden and Phylis Singer, S7
ECHOES OF BATS AND MEN–Donald R. Griffin, S4
ELECTRONS AND WAVES–John R. Pierce, S38
FARADAY, MAXWELL, AND KELVIN–D. K. C. MacDonald, S33
GRAVITY–George Gamow, S22
HEAT ENGINES–John F. Sandfort, S27
HORNS, STRINGS & HARMONY–Arthur H. Benade, S11
HOW OLD IS THE EARTH?–Patrick M. Hurley, S5
J. J. THOMSON: Discoverer of the Electron–George Thomson, S48
KNOWLEDGE AND WONDER: THE NATURAL WORLD AS MAN KNOWS IT–Victor F. Weisskopf, S31
LADY LUCK: THE THEORY OF PROBABILITY–Warren Weaver, S30
LIFE IN THE UNIVERSE–M. W. Ovenden, S23
MAGNETS–Francis Bitter, S2
MATHEMATICAL ASPECTS OF PHYSICS–Francis Bitter, S32
MICHELSON AND THE SPEED OF LIGHT–Bernard Jaffe, S13
NATURE OF VIOLENT STORMS–Louis J. Battan, S19
NEAR ZERO: THE PHYSICS OF LOW TEMPERATURE–D. K. C. MacDonald, S20

ANCHOR BOOKS

SCIENCE AND MATHEMATICS

AN APPROACH TO MODERN PHYSICS–E. N. Andrade, A111
THE BROKEN IMAGE: MAN, SCIENCE, AND SOCIETY–Floyd W. Matson, A506
DARWIN, MARX, WAGNER–Jacques Barzun, A127
DARWIN'S CENTURY–Loren Eiseley, A244
DISCOVERIES AND OPINIONS OF GALILEO–Stillman Drake, trans., A94
GIVE AND TAKE: The Biology of Tissue Transplantation–Francis D. Moore, A481
THE GREAT DOCTORS–Henry Sigerist, A140
HOW TO SOLVE IT–G. Polya, A93
THE HUMAN USE OF HUMAN BEINGS: Cybernetics and Society–Norbert Wiener, A34
THE LANGUAGE OF NATURE: An Essay on the Philosophy of Science–David Hawkins, A563
MATHEMATICS AND THE PHYSICAL WORLD–Morris Kline, A368
MEDIEVAL AND EARLY MODERN SCIENCE, Vol. I–A. C. Crombie, A167a
MEDIEVAL AND EARLY MODERN SCIENCE, Vol. II–A. C. Crombie, A167b
THE METAPHYSICAL FOUNDATIONS OF MODERN SCIENCE–Edwin Arthur Burtt, A41
MIRAGE OF HEALTH–René Dubos, A258
MODERN SCIENCE AND MODERN MAN–James B. Conant, A10
NUMBER, THE LANGUAGE OF SCIENCE–Tobias Dantzig, A67
RESEARCH PROBLEMS IN BIOLOGY: Investigations for Students–Biological Sciences Curriculum Study, Series 1, A366a
RESEARCH PROBLEMS IN BIOLOGY: Investigations for Students–Biological Sciences Curriculum Study, Series 2, A366b
RESEARCH PROBLEMS IN BIOLOGY: Investigations for Students–Biological Sciences Curriculum Study, Series 3, A366c
RESEARCH PROBLEMS IN BIOLOGY: Investigations for Students–Biological Sciences Curriculum Study, Series 4, A366d
A SHORT HISTORY OF SCIENCE–Herbert Butterfield and others, A180
STORY OF ENGINEERING–James Kip Finch, A214
UNITY OF THE UNIVERSE–D. W. Sciama, A247

NATURAL HISTORY LIBRARY

ANIMAL BEHAVIOR—John Paul Scott, N29
AUSTRALIAN ABORIGINES—A. P. Elkin, N37
BACK OF HISTORY, Revised edition—William Howells, N34
BETWEEN THE PLANETS—Fletcher G. Watson, N17
CELLS: THEIR STRUCTURE AND FUNCTION—E. H. Mercer, N25
CHARLES DARWIN—Gavin de Beer, N41
DWELLERS IN DARKNESS—S. H. Skaife, N9
EARLY MAN IN THE NEW WORLD—Kenneth Macgowan and Joseph A. Hester, N22
EXPLORATION OF THE COLORADO RIVER—John Wesley Powell, N11
FOREST PEOPLE—Colin Turnbull, N27
FROM FISH TO PHILOSOPHER—Homer W. Smith, N10
GENETICS—H. Kalmus, N38
A GUIDE TO BIRD WATCHING—Joseph J. Hickey, N30
HEATHENS—William Howells, N19
HERD OF RED DEER—F. Fraser Darling, N35
HORSES—George G. Simpson, N1
HOW TO MAKE A TELESCOPE—Jean Texereau, N31
INDIANS OF THE UNITED STATES—Clark Wissler, N42
LAND OF LITTLE RAIN—Mary Austin, A15
MARKETS IN AFRICA: Eight Subsistence Economies in Transition —Paul J. Bohannan and George Dalton, eds., N39
MODERN SCIENCE AND THE NATURE OF LIFE—William S. Beck, N8
MOUNTAINS OF CALIFORNIA—John Muir, N12
A NATURALIST IN ALASKA—Adolph Murie, N32
NAVAHO—Clyde Kluckhohn and Dorothea Leighton, N28
PACIFIC ISLANDS, Revised edition—Douglas Oliver, N14
RETURN TO LAUGHTER—Laura Marie Bohannan, N36
THE RUN—John Hay, N40
VOYAGE OF THE BEAGLE—Charles Darwin, N16
YOSEMITE—John Muir, N26